1960s Quiz Book

1,000 questions for the whole family

www.ovingo.com

Published by Ovingo Limited in 2017

For full details of other books in this series, please visit

www.ovingo.com

The golden rules of happy quizzing

1. It goes without saying that a quiz should be fun, so don't take these questions too seriously.
2. If you're playing as a group or a team, be flexible, allow for a margin of error in your friends' answers and look to give points wherever possible. Where a question asks for a year, allow a decade either way. Where it asks for a measurement, decide how big a margin to offer depending on how large or small the increments are.
3. The more generous everyone is, the more fun you'll have.

Suggested method of play for groups

To avoid anyone having to sit out and watch while one other person asks questions and another single person gives answers, appoint one question asker per round and one person who will receive all of the points from the whole team. Everyone can suggest answers and it's up to the person who receives the points to decide which answer to take (or use one of their own). At the end of the round, the question asker and the person choosing the answers should change until everyone has had a turn in each role, or you decide to stop playing.

This book is produced and published by Ovingo Limited
www.ovingo.com

Quiz 1

1 Britain and France signed an agreement to develop which iconic airliner in 1962?

2 How many times does the Beatles' song Hey Jude include the word Jude? 8, 18, 28 or 38?

3 Which action series featured the Impossible Missions Force?

4 Who released the album Viva Las Vegas in May 1964?

5 Which New York superhero, real name Peter Parker, got his special powers after being bitten by a radioactive arachnid?

6 How long did Neil Armstrong and Buzz Aldrin spend exploring the moon? 25 minutes, two and a half hours or two and a half days?

7 Which far eastern country detonated its first nuclear bomb in 1964? China, Japan or North Korea?

8 Which of The Beatles is an anagram of "Carpet Calumny"?

9 Who was Barney Rubble's next door neighbour in a TV animation that ran from 1960 until 1966?

10 At which Grand Prix track was 1960-born racing driver Ayrton Senna killed in a crash?

Quiz 2

1 How many Olympic Games were held during the 1960s? Four, six or eight?

2 Which duo released the 1966 album Sounds of Silence?

3 Which film debuted on 27 August 1964 and became its studio's biggest money-maker? Mary Poppins, The Sound of Music or My Fair Lady?

4 Who sang about A Whiter Shade of Pale in 1967?

5 Which American poet, who died in 1965, wrote Old Possum's Book of Practical Cats, and in doing so inspired the Andrew Lloyd Webber musical Cats?

6   By what name was 1963-born British singer Georgios Kyriacos Panayiotou better known?

7   Which game features prominently in the 1961 Paul Newman film, The Hustler? Darts, Bowling or Pool?

8   Which double-decker aeroplane did Boeing unveil in September 1968?

9   Who played Doctor Zhivago in the 1965 film of the same name?

10 What was the name of the Welsh village in which the 1967 TV series The Prisoner was filmed? Porthmadog, Porthgain or Portmeirion?

Quiz 3

1   What was the occupation of American-born Sylvia Plath, who committed suicide in London in February 1963?

2   How many airlines flew Concorde aircraft following its introduction in 1969? Two, Four or Eight?

3   Whose album, The Times They Are a-Changin', was released in 1964? Bob Dylan, Bo Diddley or Burt Bacharach?

4   1964's A Shot in the Dark was the second film in which Peter Sellers series?

5   Who wrote the book on which the 1963 film Oliver was based?

6   Which country hosted the 1962 FIFA World Cup? Brazil, Chile or Argentina?

7   True or false: Harry S Truman was president of the United States at the start of the 1960s?

8   Who wrote and recorded Puppy Love in 1960? Paul Anka or Donny Osmond?

9   Name the 1967-born singer and big band leader who starred in the films Memphis Belle and Independence Day.

10 Which future James Bond actor was born in Cheshire in 1968?

Quiz 4

1 Which country's first television station started broadcasting on 1 June 1960? New Zealand, Australia or China?

2 Which suave Brit was the lead character in the 1968 novel Colonel Sun, written by Kingsley Amis under the pseudonym Robert Markham?

3 Find the name of an astronaut in the anagram "Morning Alerts".

4 Which US president was born in Hawaii in August 1961?

5 Which actor, born in 1964, starred in Leaving Las Vegas and Captain Corelli's Mandolin, and was married to both Patricia Arquette and Lisa Marie Presley?

6 How many astronauts could fit in the Apollo space capsules that NASA used throughout the 1960s? One, three or five?

7 Of which group was Brian Jones a founder, before drowning in a pool in July 1969?

8 To what did Robert Allen Zimmerman change his name in August 1962? David Bowie, Bob Dylan or Keith Richards?

9 Which cartoon series about a cat and a mouse made its television debut in September 1965?

10 Where was actor Kenneth Branagh born in December 1960? Belfast, Birmingham or Bermuda?

Quiz 5

1 In which year did the first ever Paralympic Games take place? 1960, 1964 or 1968?

2 Which long-running British TV series debuted in December 1960? Last of the Summer Wine, Doctor Who or Coronation Street?

3 Which animated TV comedy set in 2062 debuted 100 years earlier in 1962?

4   At which jewellery store was Audrey Hepburn having breakfast in the 1961 film also starring George Peppard?

5   Which musician and activist's daughter, Moon Unit, was born in 1967?

6   Elvis Presley returned to the US after two years' military service in 1960. Where had he been posted? Germany, Vietnam or Korea?

7   The head of which famous statue, an icon of the city, was stolen from Copenhagen harbour in April 1964?

8   Name the 1964 Michael Caine film that told the story of the 1879 Battle of Rorke's Drift?

9   Which Kennedy brother entered the race for the Democratic Party nominee for president in March 1968?

10   NASA sent its Ranger 3 probe to the moon in 1962, but it missed by how many miles? 22 miles, 220 miles or 22,000 miles?

Quiz 6

1   Which Canadian-American actor, born in 1969, played Chandler Bing in the TV series Friends?

2   Nigel Clayton and Bono, who were both born in 1960, went on to form which supergroup?

3   Which TCC was the Liverpool venue where The Beatles performed together for the first time?

4   In the book of Mary Poppins, she looks after five children: Jane, Michael, John, Barbara and Annabel. Only two of them appear in the 1964 film. Which two?

5   Who starred as Melanie Daniels in Alfred Hitchcock's 1963 movie, The Birds?

6   What kind of car was Herbie in 1968's The Love Bug?

7   Which 1969-born Texan played the title character in the Bridget Jones series of films?

8   What was the 60s' top-grossing film: Spartacus, Psycho, Exodus?

9   Which British actor, born in 1963, played Robert Crawley, Lord Grantham, in British TV series Downton Abbey?

10   With whom did Margot Fonteyn dance for the first time at the Royal Ballet in February 1962?

Quiz 7

1   Name the British rock band, which is an anagram of "Hollering Stetson".

2   How old was Robert F Kennedy when assassinated in 1968? 38, 42 or 44?

3   In which year did the Cuban Missile Crisis take place? 1962, 1964 or 1966?

4   Of which film, starring Audrey Hepburn and Rex Harrison, is "Arid Mayfly" an anagram?

5   Which supersonic aircraft was unveiled in Toulouse in December 1967?

6   For what did Brits Bryan Whitby and SC Cummins file a patent application in 1965, which has since become the global standard? Ice cream vans, high speed internet or air conditioning?

7   Which groundbreaking animator died of a tumour on his lung in December 1966?

8   Name the English novelist, born in November 1960, whose work includes American Gods and The Ocean at the End of the Lane?

9   Which group hit number 1 in the US charts with Where Did Our Love Go, in August 1964?

10   Who played the title role in the 1963 movie, Cleopatra?

Quiz 8

1   Which former presenter of BBC Top Gear was born in Yorkshire, England, in April 1960?

2 Which American comedian was born in 1961 and appeared in the films Beverly Hills Cop, Trading Places and The Nutty Professor?

3 Which British wartime leader retired from the House of Commons in 1964, aged 89?

4 By what nickname was Leonard McCoy, the Star Trek doctor, also known?

5 Which number was pained on Herbie in the 1968 film The Love Bug? 33, 43 or 53?

6 Which musical producer and songwriter, whose work appeared in Oklahoma, South Pacific and The Sound of Music, died in August 1960?

7 Did Americans go to the moon once, twice or three times during the 1960s?

8 Complete the title of Roald Dahl's 1961 children's book: James and the Giant...

9 Who sang These Boots are Made for Walkin' in 1966?

10 Which music manager's name can be found by unscrambling the letters in "Tenpin Serbia"?

Quiz 9

1 When did the Woodstock Festival take place? 1965, 1967 or 1969?

2 Who wrote To Kill a Mocking Bird, published in 1960?

3 What was the name of the boy brought up by animals in the 1967 Disney film, The Jungle Book?

4 What nationality is Mads Mikkelsen, the 1965-born actor who played Le Chiffre in Bond film Casino Royale? Danish, Swedish or Norwegian?

5 Which Russian city was renamed Volgograd on 11 November 1961? St Petersburg, Vladivostok or Stalingrad?

6 Which film director, born in England in 1965, directed American Beauty, Skyfall and Spectre?

7   Which 1964-born actor, the daughter of Peter and granddaughter of Henry, starred in the films Single White Female Jackie Brown and The Godfather Part III?

8   Which 1969 book by Paul Gallico tells the story of a luxury ocean liner that is capsized by a massive underwater earthquake, and was filmed three years later starring Gene Hackman, Shelley Winters and Leslie Nielsen?

9   Name the Australian actor, born in Britain in 1967, who starred in the soap Neighbours, and the films LA Confidential, The King's Speech and The Adventures of Priscilla, Queen of the Desert.

10   In which city did the Stonewall riots of June 1969 take place: New York, Chicago or San Francisco?

Quiz 10

1   In which year was Jon Bon Jovi, lead singer of Bon Jovi, born? 1960, 1962 or 1964?

2   Which long-running comedy series about rag and bone men debuted on British TV in 1962 and was later remade as Sanford and Son in the US, and Albert & Herbert in Sweden?

3   Which country opened the world's first stretch of high speed railway line, for its Bullet Train, in 1964?

4   Who is the Icelandic singer, songwriter, DJ, producer and actress who was born in 1965 and first found fame as the lead singer in The Sugarcubes?

5   Which music superstar was killed in Tennessee in 1963 when her plane crashed?

6   In which city was Martin Luther King Jr assassinated in April 1968? Memphis, Minneapolis or Milwaukee?

7   Who wrote the 1962 book A Clockwork Orange, partly in a fictional secret language called Nadsat?

8   Which PG was the decidedly non-PG name of a 1960s Bond girl?

9   Which TV family lives at 0001 Cemetery Lane in a two-season comedy initially aired between 1964 and 1966?

10   What did Valentina Tereshkova become the first woman to do in 1963?

Quiz 11

1   Which Steve McQueen thriller of 1968 includes an 11 minute car chase considered to be one of the best film chases of all time?

2   Which ballet dancer's name is an anagram of "Unloved Furry"?

3   What did the US government declare may be hazardous to health for the first time in January 1964?

4   Which British double agent was given asylum in Russia in July 1963?

5   Which of these was not a film from 1961? The Man-Trap, The Parent Trap or The Mousetrap?

6   Bobbi Gibb was the first woman to run which marathon? Sydney, London or Boston?

7   In which comedy drama was 1963-born singer Vonda Shepard a regular between 1997 and 2002?

8   Which Welsh singer's July 1968 album release was entitled Delilah after one of his best-known songs?

9   By what name is Irish group U2's 1961-born guitarist David Howell Evans better known?

10   Which US police serial debuted on 20 September 1968 and ran until 1980? Hill Street Blues, Law & Order, or Hawaii Five-O?

Quiz 12

1   In March 1969, who did James Earl Ray plead guilty to assassinating? Martin Luther King Jr or Robert F Kennedy?

2   What did the US officially abolish in July 1964? Prohibition, Conscription or Segregation?

3   CERN switched on its first particle accelerator in February 1960. Where is CERN based?

4   Which stop-animation children's programme, featuring characters living in an enchanted wood, ran for 441 five-minute episodes and was originally called Le Manege Enchante?

5   Tim Cook, was born in November 1960, and went on to run which US electronics company following the death of its founder in 2011?

6   Which iconic pop artist painted a tin of Campbell's Soup in 1960?

7   Which British actor, born in Lancashire in 1964, played Bubble in the BBC sitcom Absolutely Fabulous, and was nominated for BAFTAs and Golden Globes for Little Voice?

8   Adam Clayton and Bono, both of U2, were both in 1960. Which is younger?

9   Which Soviet leader's daughter defected to the US in March 1967? Stalin, Lenin or Trotsky?

10 Which author, who died in 1969, wrote The Day of The Triffids, Chocky, The Kraken Wakes and The Midwich Cuckoos?

Quiz 13

1   Which former British prime minister, born in 1966, served as leader from 2010, and left in 2016 following the country's referendum to leave the European Union?

2   Which 1965-born actor is best known for playing Carrie Bradshaw in Sex and the City?

3   From what did boxer Muhammad Ali change his name in 64?

4   Which car manufacturer introduced the world to the iconic 911 for the first time in 1963?

5   What kind of animal was Shere Khan in the 1967 film The Jungle Book?

6   Which American actor, born in 1968, starred in A Few Good Men, Jerry Maguire and Pearl Harbour? His first name is the name of a country.

7   Which country's prime minister, Hendrik Verwoerd, was stabbed to death in parliament in September 1966? The Netherlands, Belgium or South Africa?

8   Which actor, who won Oscars for The French Connection and Unforgiven, and played Lex Luthor in Superman The Movie, made his cinema debut in 1961's Mad Dog Coll?

9   Three countries launched rockets in 1965. The United States and Soviet Union were two. Who was the third? China, India, France or Japan?

10   The world's first ATM, or cash machine, went into operation in London in which year? 1965, 1967 or 1969?

Quiz 14

1   Which 1963-born American singer is known for Fields of Gold and Over the Rainbow, and died of cancer in 1996?

2   Which character did 1968-born actor Gillian Anderson play in sci-fi serial The X-Files?

3   In which year did Yuri Gagarin become the first man in space? 1961, 1963 or 1965?

4   Which 1964-born actor came to prominence in films like St Elmo's Fire and The Outsiders, and the TV show The West Wing, where he played Sam Seaborn?

5   Which 1964 satire, directed by Stanley Kubrick, was sub-titled How I Learned to Stop Worrying and Love the Bomb?

6   Which duo composed the 1961 film West Side Story?

7   Which actor, who played Gandalf the Grey in Peter Jackson's Lord of the Rings films, first appeared on cinema screens in 1969's Thank You All Very Much?

8   Which British actor, born in 1960, played King George VI in The King's Speech, as well as roles in Bridget Jones' Diary, Shakespeare in Love and Love Actually?

9   Which former governor of Alaska, who ran for Vice President in the 2008 US Presidential Election, was born in Idaho in 1964?

10 Who starred as Lawrence of Arabia in the 1962 film of the same name?

Quiz 15

1   What make of car was Kennedy travelling in when he was assassinated in 1963? Lincoln, Ford or General Motors?

2   Which European city hosted the 1960 Summer Olympic Games? Paris, London or Rome?

3   Who married Cynthia Powell in an unpublicised register office ceremony at Mount Pleasant, Liverpool in August 1962? Ringo Starr, John Lennon, Paul McCartney or George Harrison?

4   Who starred in the title role of the 1966 British romantic comedy drama film, Alfie?

5   In which country was tennis player Ivan Lendl born in 1960? Yugoslavia, Poland or Czechoslovakia?

6   Name the 1982 film starring Harrison Ford and directed by Ridley Scott, which was based on Philip K Dick's 1968 novel Do Androids Dream of Electric Sheep.

7   Peri Gilpin (as Roz) and Jane Leeves (as Daphne) both appeared in Frasier and were both born in 1961. Which is older?

8   Which duo initially performed under the name Tom & Jerry in the 1950s before finding international success in the 60s under their own names?

9   Which guerrilla leader and primary figure in the Cuban Revolution was assassinated in 1967?

10   Which 1965 comedy starring Peter Sellers, Peter O'Toole and Ursula Andress about a man who desperately wants to be faithful to his fiancee, marked Woody Allen's first cinema acting appearance?

Quiz 16

1   Which children's author, who created The Secret Seven, The Famous Five and Noddy, among others, died in London, aged 71, in November 1968?

2   Which American singer, born in 1963, was known for I Wanna Dance with Somebody and How Will I know, and starred in the romantic thriller The Bodyguard?

3   In which decade was the 1961 movie West Side Story set? The 40s, 50s or 60s?

4   Which band had its first US number one hit with 1965's I Can't Get No Satisfaction?

5   Who was the second man to walk on the moon?

6   Which 1961-born actress played Sammy Jo Carrington in Dynasty, Stacy Sheridan in TJ Hooker, and Amanda Woodware in Melrose Place?

7   Which Australian singer and actor, known for the songs Locomotion, I Should Be So Lucky and Can't Get You Out Of My Head, was born in Melbourne in May 1968?

8   Which Australian director, born in 1962, made the films Moulin Rouge and Strictly Ballroom?

9   The Beatles got to number 1 in the US charts for the first time in February 1964. What was the song? She Loves You, I Want to Hold Your Hand or Help?

10   What is the job of Jean Brodie in Muriel Spark's 1961 novel, The Prime of Miss Jean Brodie?

Quiz 17

1 Who starred as Rosemary in the 1968 film, Rosemary's Baby? Mia Farrow, Anne Bancroft or Angela Lansbury?

2 Of what was Arpanet, the network introduced by the US military in 1969, the forerunner?

3 Where did Patrick McGoohan's character, Number Six, live in the 1967 TV series, The Prisoner? The Hamlet, The Community or The Village?

4 What nationality is 1966-born tennis player Stefan Edberg? Swedish, German or Austrian?

5 What was the family name of the singing children in the 1965 film The Sound of Music?

6 Which future Bond villain, and star of Annie Hall, The Deer Hunter, Pulp Fiction and Hairspray, made his debut in 1966's Barefoot in Athens?

7 What is the brand name of the artificial grass, popular on sports pitches, that was introduced in 1965?

8 Which country pulled out of NATO in March 1966? France, Spain or Italy?

9 Which postal song by Elvis Presley was the biggest-selling single of 1962?

10 Who released a 1963 compilation album called Ring of Fire after one of his best-known songs?

Quiz 18

1 Who wrote the screenplay and thriller Where Eagles Dare?

2 Name the actor born in 1968 who would go on to play Saffron Monsoon in BBC comedy Absolutely Fabulous.

3 To whom was Priscilla Beaulieu married in May 1967?

4 Which global online superstore did 1964-born American entrepreneur Jeff Bezos go on to found?

5   What was the name of the policeman who featured in the early-1960s animated series, Top Cat?

6   How long had Elvis Presley served in the army when he returned to music in 1960? Two years, four years or six years?

7   Which 1964-born US novelist is best known for his book, American Psycho?

8   The first man in space got there in 1961. When did the first woman get to space? 1961, 1963 or 1965?

9   What was the codename of the Ice Station in the title of the 1963 film starring Rock Hudson and Patrick McGoohan? Zero, Zulu or Zebra?

10   The New York times made the world's first recorded use of which technical term in November 1962? Internet, personal computer, or mobile phone?

Quiz 19

1   Which CCBB was a magical car dreamed up by Ian Fleming?

2   Which Canadian model and actress, known for Baywatch and Home Improvement, was born in British Columbia in 67?

3   How many days did the Cuban Missile Crisis take to resolve? 11, 12 or 13?

4   Which 1965 film features the songs Climb Every Mountain, Edelweiss and The Lonely Goatherd?

5   Who was hospitalised as a result of a head-on car collision just as her song I Fall to Pieces became a big hit in 1961? Patsy Cline, Cilla Black or Cher?

6   Who was born in August 1960 and went on to star as Fox Mulder in The X Files?

7   The programming language BASIC was introduced in 1964. What did BASIC stand for?

8   What was the official title of Mao Zedong, who led China's Cultural Revolution from 1966?

9 Which actor, born in Malaga, Spain, in August 1960, was married to Melanie Griffith and starred in Evita, The Mask of Zorro, and as Puss in Boots in the Shrek films?

10 Who was the first prime minister of Vietnam, who died in 1969, and after whom Saigon was renamed?

Quiz 20

1 About which book did British judge Mervyn Griffith-Jones say, in 1960, "Is it a book that you would ever wish your wife or your servants to read?"

2 Spartacus, Dr Strangelove and 2001: A Space Odyssey, all films of the 1960s that share a director. Who?

3 Which series, debuting in 1963, followed Dr Richard Kimble as he ran from the law following his conviction for murder?

4 Which country announced in 1968 that it was going to phase out its entire force of aircraft carriers? The United Kingdom, Italy or Greece?

5 Two men stood on the moon during the first manned expedition there in 1969. How many people were on the mission in total?

6 Which country became independent of France in July 1962? Algeria, Morocco or Libya?

7 Which 1968 heist film starring Steve McQueen and Faye Dunaway won an Oscar for the song Windmills of Your Mind?

8 Name the character played by Anthony Perkins in the 1960 psychological horror, Psycho.

9 Which PMP, sung by The Marvelettes, was the Motown record label's first number one hit?

10 How many leap years were there in the 1960s?

Quiz 21

1   Whose body was removed from the Lenin Mausoleum on 31 October 1961? Lenin, Stalin or Trotsky?

2   Who said that he and his friends were "more popular than Jesus now" during a 1966 interview with the London Evening Standard?

3   Which star of The Graduate actually made his cinema debut in another film released the same year, called The Tiger Makes Out?

4   Which 1965 war film tells the story of a group of Allied prisoners who hijack a train and flee through German-occupied Italy to Switzerland?

5   Whose compilation album, The Dock of the Bay, named after one of his most famous songs, went on sale in February 1968?

6   Which British soprano was born in 1960 and was married to the composer Andrew Lloyd Webber from 1984 until 1990?

7   Who became the first man in space when he left earth's atmosphere in 1961?

8   Which comedy ran from 1965 until 1970 and featured Barbara Eden as a 2000 year old genie and Larry Hagman as an astronaut?

9   Which TAF lived in Cemetery Lane?

10 Which James Bond film, the second in the series, premiered in the US in April 1964? Dr No, From Russia With Love or Goldfinger?

Quiz 22

1   Which actor, born in 1965, is famed for playing the character Alan Partridge, and appearing in the films The

Parole Officer, 24 Hour Party People, and Around the World in 80 Days?

2   British prime minister Harold Wilson's I'm Backing Britain campaign of 1968 asked Brits to do what? Work half an hour extra every day for free, sign up for National Service or take good care of their backs?

3   How many days was the Woodstock festival scheduled to run for?

4   What was the name of Fred and Betty Flintstone's daughter?

5   Complete the title of Dionne Warwick's 1967 single: "I Say..."

6   Which actress married Richard Burton in March 1964?

7   Which American actor, born in 1960, first appeared in Little House on the Prairie, but is better known for Mystic River, Milk, and for being married to Madonna?

8   Which organ did Christiaan Barnard transplant for the first time in a human in 1967?

9   Which Charlton Heston film of 1959 won the Oscar for Best Picture at the 1960 Academy Awards?

10   Which motor company produced the first of its Mustang cars on 9 March 1964?

Quiz 23

1   Which actress married Peter Sellers on 19 February 1964?

2   What, in 1963, became the most expensive film ever made up until that time? Ben-Hur, Cleopatra or The Sound of Music?

3   Complete the title of the 1969 film: Butch Cassidy and...

4   Name the group fronted by Eric Burdon that smashed America with 1964's House of the Rising Sun.

5   In which city is Candlestick Park where, in 1966, The Beatles gave their last ever concert?

6   What was the top-grossing film of 1964: Mary Poppins, Goldfinger or My Fair Lady?

7   Which 1969 novel by John Fowles was set in the mid-19th century, in the English coastal town of Lyme Regis and tells the story of a man who falls in love with a former governess, later adapted for film starring Meryl Streep and Jeremy Irons?

8   Iran, Iraq, Kuwait, Saudi Arabia and Venezuela formed OPEC in September 1960. Where is it based? Vienna, Rome or Geneva?

9   Did Agatha Christie's 1962 book, The Mirror Crack'd From Side to Side, feature Hercule Poirot or Miss Marple?

10 Which 1964 Roy Orbison single tells the story of a man who sees an attractive lady on the street?

Quiz 24

1   Henry Fonda and Dennis Hopper's characters in the 1969 film Easy Rider funded their road trip by selling what? Cocaine, alcohol or guns?

2   Which British band member's first book, In His Own Write, was published on 24 March 1964?

3   Name the US film director, born in 1966, who is responsible for Armageddon, Star Trek Into Darkness, Cloverfield and Star Wars: The Force Awakens.

4   What was the only European country not to broadcast Winston Churchill's 1965 funeral live on TV? Germany, France or the Republic of Ireland?

5   Who sang, in 1966, about "these boots", which were "made for walkin'"?

6   Who created the genre of Folk Rock when they released a cover of Bob Dylan's Mr Tambourine Man, which got to number 1 in both the UK and the US?

7   Which 1963-born Russian chess player was ranked world number 1 for 225 out of 228 months between 1986 and his retirement in 2005?

8   Which novelist, renowned for inventing the character James Bond, died aged 56 in August 1964?

9   Which American actor, who featured in Romancing The Stone, Wall Street and Behind the Candelabra, made his cinema debut in the 1966 film Cast a Giant Shadow?

10   Which series of five-digit numbers was introduced in the United States in July 1963?

Quiz 25

1   Name the Canadian singer, born in 1968, who sang The Power of Love, Think Twice and My Heart Will Go On.

2   Which 1962-born actor starred in the films War Games, Ferris Bueller's Day Off and The Producers?

3   What was the name of Honor Blackman's character in the 1964 movie Goldfinger?

4   Jackie Stewart, Graham Hill and John Surtees, who took the first three places in the 1968 United States Grand Prix, are all drivers from which country?

5   When Elvis Presley returned to music in 60 after two years in the army, he released two songs. Name either of them.

6   Which 1963 film starring Richard Burton and Elizabeth Taylor became the biggest box office disaster in cinema history for being the highest grossing title of the year but still losing money because of the astronomical cost of production?

7   Name the American cartoon producer who died in 1965, best known for introducing Tom and Jerry to the world.

8   Who fronted The Doors, which released its debut, self-titled, album in 1966?

9   What is the stage name of 1967-born musician, actor and rapper Robert Matthew Van Winkle?

10   Which iconic car, popular throughout the 1960s and beyond, was designed by Sir Alec Issigonis in the late 1950s?

Quiz 26

1   Which European landmark did American Robert P McCulloch buy on 1 April 1968? The Eiffel Tower, The Brandenburg Gate or London Bridge?

2   Construction of which historical barrier began on 13 August 1961?

3   Which country announced that it was going to annex Kuwait in June 1961?

4   Marcia Cross and Felicity Huffman were both born in 1962, and both starred in Desperate Housewives. Which of them played Lynette Scavo?

5   Which Canadian TV show about a problem solving German Shepherd dog ran from 1963 until 1965?

6   Which 1961 book by Joseph Heller follows the life of US Army Air Forces bombardier John Yossarian on the island of Pianosa?

7   Complete this phrase from a speech given by John F Kennedy on 26 June 1963: "Ich bin ein…"

8   Sarah Jessica Parker and Matthew Broderick are both film stars, both born in the 1960s, and married to each other. Which is older?

9   Which US president's wife was pregnant while he was running for office in 1960?

10   In which US state was the Woodstock festival held?

Quiz 27

1   On what part of her body might a woman have worn a beehive when they became popular in the 1960s?

2   Who did 1964-born actor Calista Flockhart play from 1997 until 2002 in a surreal US comedy drama about Boston legal professionals?

3   Whose 1964 album was called A Bit of Liverpool? Was it The Beatles, The Supremes or The Rolling Stones?

4   How many days after assassinating President Kennedy was Lee Harvey Oswald himself killed by Jack Ruby?

5   After which Greek god, the god of light, music and the sun, did NASA name the space capsules it used in the 1960s, and the accompanying space programme?

6   Which American film director of Reservoir Dogs, Kill Bill and Pulp Fiction was born in Tennessee in March 1963?

7   Which American producer, singer and songwriter was born in May 1964 and is known by many for his 1993 hit Are You Gonna Go My Way?

8   Which actor, born in 1966, played Queen Elizabeth in The King's Speech and Mrs Bucket in Charlie and the Chocolate Factory, and was married to both Kenneth Brannagh and Tim Burton?

9   Did the 1964 Winter Olympics take place in Germany, Austria or Switzerland?

10   Why was 1961 declared an "upside down" year?

Quiz 28

1   Which Canadian choreographer was born in 1962 and hit the charts in 1989 with the song Opposites Attract?

2   When was the first leap year in the 1960s?

3   Of the four men who served as US president during the 60s – Eisenhower, Kennedy, Johnson and Nixon – who had the longest retirement?

4   Which 1967-born American singer is known for the hits Unbreak My Heart, Breathe Again and Another Sad Love Song?

5   Which boxer was stripped of his World Heavyweight Champion titles and banned from boxing when he refused to be inducted into the United States Army in May 1967?

6　Which country chose a red and white design bearing an 11-pointed maple leaf as its new flag in 1964, and implemented it the following year?

7　Which 1960-born novelist created Inspector Rebus, and wrote a series of novels about the character?

8　When the series debuted in 1966, who was the communications officer on Star Trek's first USS Enterprise?

9　Who wrote the 1969 book The Very Hungry Caterpillar, which taught children how to count?

10　In the month after whose death in 1962, from a barbiturate overdose, did the suicide rate in Los Angeles double?

Quiz 29

1　How did Ironside, the lead character in the TV series of the same name, come to have been paralysed, leaving him in a wheelchair?

2　Who, in 1967, performed the first heart transplant?

3　Name the club, the first rule of which is that you don't talk about it, that featured in a book by 1962-born novelist Chuck Palahniuk.

4　Whose application for membership of the United Nations did the Soviet Union veto in November 1961? Iran, Iraq or Kuwait?

5　Who released an album called Abbey Road in 1969?

6　Which British comedy series, debuting in 1969 and running until 1994, had a distinctive theme tune called Yakety Sax, and became one of Britain's most successful TV exports, airing in 97 other countries?

7　Name the country singer born in 1965 who sang You're Still The One, and Man I Feel Like a Woman.

8　Name the 1961-born Irish singer who was a member of Celtic band Clannad and had solo albums called Dark Sky Island and Watermark.

9　Was John F Kennedy president of the United States before or after Richard Nixon?

10　Which actor, who would later play a leading role in seven James Bond films, made her cinema debut in 1964's The Third Secret?

Quiz 30

1　How many Pink Panther films were released in the 1960s? One, two or three?

2　Who was the lead singer of REM, who was born on 4 January 1960?

3　Which BAT starred Audrey Hepburn, George Peppard and a renowned jewellery store?

4　Which handy computer peripheral was first demonstrated by Douglas Engelbart in December 1968?

5　Which Dutch artist created Waterfall in 1961, a lithograph in which water appears to flow downhill along a path with raised edges before reaching the top of a waterfall?

6　Why was the Sea of Tranquility of great interest in July 1969?

7　In which year was the world's first WalMart store opened? 1962, 1965 or 1968?

8　Which 1961-born actress, best known for her portrayal of Amanda Carrington in 1980s soap Dynasty, is the daughter of Princess Elizabeth of Yugoslavia?

9　Which country chose Alexander Dubcek as the leader of its Communist Party, and thus of the country itself, in January 1968? The Soviet Union, Bulgaria or Czechoslovakia?

10　How did Berlin resident Ida Siekmann earn a place in history on 22 August 1961?

Quiz 31

1 Which singer, best known for the song Sittin' on The Dock of The Bay, died aged 26 in a 1967 plane crash?

2 When was the last ever Looney Tunes cartoon released? 1960, 1964 or 1968?

3 What major change to its traffic laws did Sweden make at 5am on 3 September 1967?

4 How many of The Beatles' 22 studio albums were released in the 1960s?

5 What time of day was John F Kennedy assassinated? 9.30am, 12.30pm or 6.30pm?

6 Which television western series starring Eric Fleming and Clint Eastwood came to the end of its run of eight seasons in January 1966, after 217 episodes?

7 How many presidents had been assassinated before Kennedy was shot and killed in 1963?

8 Which British pop singer appeared in films called Wonderful Life, The Young Ones and Summer holiday between 1961 and 1964?

9 Was Dwight D Eisenhower president of the United States before or after Lyndon B Johnson?

10 In which city did the Scottish Gallery of National Art open in 1960? Edinburgh, Glasgow or Aberdeen?

Quiz 32

1 In which country did the world's first Automatic Teller Machine (ATM or cash machine) go into operation in 1967?

2 Which British singer released an album called 21 Today on 14 October 1961, his 21st birthday? Cliff Richard, Mick Jagger or David Bowie?

3 Which 1963-born actor gained recognition for appearing

in Thelma & Louise, featured in Oceans 11, 12 and 13, and starred in the cult movie Fight Club?

4   Which 1967 album was nicknamed "The soundtrack to the Summer of Love"?

5   Which American actor, who would later star in Overboard and Private Benjamin, had her cinema debut in the 1968 film The One and Only, Genuine, Original Family Brand?

6   Who became leader of the Soviet Union in 1966? Nikita Khrushchev, Leonid Brezhnev or Yuri Andropov?

7   By what name is 1962-born William Bruce Rose Jr better known?

8   Which of the Marx Brothers died in September 1964? Harpo, Groucho or Zeppo?

9   What day of the week was the last day of the 1960s?

10   Which actor, who would go on to play the Terminator and become Governor of California, made his cinema debut in 1969, in Hercules in New York?

Quiz 33

1   In which year did The Beatles first visit the US and perform on the Ed Sullivan Show? Was it 1962, 1964 or 1966?

2   Name the car that featured in the 1968 film, The Love Bug.

3   Which British racing driver, who set records for being the fastest person on both land and water, died in 1967 while attempting to set another record in Bluebird K7 on Coniston Water?

4   Who was leader of the Soviet Union throughout the 1962 Cuban Missile Crisis?

5   Which member of the Friends cast was born in 1967 and went on to front the BBC's Top Gear motoring show?

6   Which item of clothing first went on sale in a shop called Bazaar on London's King's Road in 1965, and quickly became a global phenomenon?

7   Who directed the 1963 suspense film, The Birds?

8   Whose 1967 book, One Hundred Years of Solitude, has since become a modern classic?

9   Wavey Leaseholder is an anagram of which killer's name?

10   Which country dropped four nuclear bombs on Iceland when it crashed one of its planes there? The Soviet Union, China or the United States?

Quiz 34

1   Of the four men who served as US president during the 60s – Eisenhower, Kennedy, Johnson and Nixon – who had the shortest tenure?

2   The Sherman Brothers won Grammys and double Oscars for which film soundtrack of the 1960s? Mary Poppins, The Sound of Music, or Bedknobs and Broomsticks?

3   Which European country saw mass student uprisings in 1968? Italy, Germany or France?

4   Find the name of an author, known for the book A Clockwork Orange, found in the anagram "Nearby Gunshots".

5   Which BBC presenter was born in Lancashire in 1966 and presented the corporation's Top Gear motoring programme for one series following the departure of Jeremy Clarkson?

6   Which actor, who played the father in Chitty Chitty Bang Bang and chimney sweep in Mary Poppins, made his cinema debut in Bye Bye Birdie in 1961?

7   Who wrote The Prime of Miss Jean Brodie in 1961?

8   In which European country was a dictatorship founded in 1967 following a military coup? Greece, Italy or Spain?

9   By the time it closed in 1963, how many years had Alcatraz prison been in operation? 29, 129 or 229?

10   Which boxer, who reigned as the undisputed world heavyweight champion and holds the record as the

youngest boxer ever to win a heavyweight title, was born in New York in June 1966?

Quiz 35

1   Name the Richard Burton film of 1965, based on a book by John Le Carre, in which Burton plays a British spy sent to sow disinformation in Cold War East Germany.

2   What was the name of Frasier Crane's producer, in the TV series Frasier, played by 1961-born Peri Gilpin?

3   Which actor, born in 1962, played "Maverick" Mitchell in Top Gun?

4   If Eleanor Rigby was the B-side, what was on the A side of The Beatles 1966 single, which reached number 1 in the UK, Canada, Netherlands, Norway, Germany, Ireland, New Zealand, Australia and Austria?

5   Which British actor, singer and songwriter died in 1961 but will always be remembered for playing his ukulele to songs like When I'm Cleaning Windows?

6   Whose last ever film, A Countess from Hong Kong, was released in 1967? Charlie Chaplin, Harold Lloyd or Laurel and Hardy?

7   Which American supermodel was born in 1966, married Richard Gere and was named One of the Hottest Women of All Time by Men's Health magazine in 2011?

8   Which major agreement did the United States, United Kingdom and Soviet Union sign in January 1967? The Underwater Treaty, The Antarctic Treaty or The Outer Space Treaty?

9   Which fast food chain was founded in March 1962 in Dowey, California? Taco Bell, Subway or McDonalds?

10 What was the nationality of the first man in space, who got there in 1961?

Quiz 36

1 The only ever colour episode of which TV drama series was broadcast on 27 February 1966? The Addams Family, Perry Mason or Bonanza?

2 Who played Spartacus in the 1960 film of the same name? Laurence Olivier, Tony Curtis or Kirk Douglas?

3 Who played Mark Anthony to Elizabeth Taylor's Cleopatra in the 1963 film of the same name?

4 Which entry in the long-running Carry On film series hit cinemas in 1960: Carry on Girls, Carry on Doctor or Carry on Constable?

5 Which husband and wife singing duo had their first number one in 1965 with I Got You Babe?

6 What was Mister Ed in the TV series of the same name that ran from 1961 until 1966?

7 Which WSS was a tale about Sharks and Jets?

8 Who led the small group of army officers who overthrew the Libyan monarchy in 1969 and went on to rule the country for several decades?

9 Which British tennis player won the 1968 US Open Women's Single event?

10 Aleksandr Solzhenitsyn's novella One Day in the Life of Ivan Denisovich, published in 1962, told the story of the lead character's experiences where? The Mir space station, a gulag or the Moscow subway?

Quiz 37

1 Which SAG sang about the Sound of Silence?

2 Why was a French character called Schuss frequently on global television for two weeks in 1968?

3   Untangle the anagram "Tanned Salami" to find the maiden name of one of the Beatles' wives.

4   Which group was originally called the Blackjacks, then the Quarrymen, before finding fame under the name by which they're now known?

5   Which British band featuring Brian Jones, Keith Richard, Bill Wyman and Mick Jagger, released its debut album in April 1964?

6   How many Dalmatians featured in a 1961 Disney animation?

7   What is the full name of J.Lo, the American singer, actress and dancer born in 1969, whose debut number one single was If You Had My Love?

8   What was Telstar?

9   Which 1962 biopic told the story of TE Lawrence?

10   Whose debut album, released in 1964, was called Stay Awhile/I Only Want to Be with You?

Quiz 38

1   Which duo, known for Unchained Melody and You've Lost that Lovin' Feeling, disbanded in 68 but reunited in the mid-70s?

2   Who was the deaf-blind author, activist and lecturer, the first deaf-blind person to earn a bachelor of arts degree, who died on 1 June 1968?

3   Which DZ was a 1965 film starring Omar Sharif and Julie Christie?

4   Where did Lyndon B Johnson send soldiers when given authority to do so by the Gulf of Tonkin Resolution in August 1964?

5   Who played Charlie Croker in the 1969 film, The Italian Job?

6   Who directed the 1964 movie Doctor Strangelove?

7   Which London-based designer is credited with inventing the mini skirt in the 1960s?

8   French singer Edith Piaf died in October 1963. What does Piaf mean? Sparrow, Robin, Thrush or Starling?

9   Who is the 1965-born American actor who starred in Young Guns, Platoon and Wall Street, and is the brother of Emilio Estevez?

10 Love is a Funny Thing, which debuted in 1969, marked the first cinema appearance of which Texan actor, who later starred in The Six Million Dollar Man with her husband Lee Majors?

Quiz 39

1   Which blonde film star was granted a divorce from dramatist Arthur Miller in January 1961 on the grounds of incompatibility?

2   Which Julie Andrews film premiered at New York's Rivoli theatre on 2 March 1965? The Sound of Music or Mary Poppins?

3   Which American actor, born in 1967, found fame in the film Pretty Woman, and has since starred in Steel Magnolias, Hook and Notting Hill?

4   Which 1962-born actress played Clarice Starling in Silence of the Lambs?

5   What is the name of Elvis Presley's daughter, born in February 1968, who is herself a musician and actor?

6   Which British band announced the creation of its own Apple Records label on 14 May 1968?

7   Actor, producer and businesswoman Wendy Deng, born in 1968, became the third wife of which Australian media mogul in 1999?

8   In 1968, which show broadcast the first interracial kiss on US television? Star Trek, Diff'rent Strokes or Hawaii Five-O?

9   Which Australian actress, who starred in Moulin Rouge, Days of Thunder and Australia was born in Hawaii in 1967?

10 Whose government did US forces attempt to overthrow with the 1961 Bay of Pigs invasion?

Quiz 40

1 Which American actor and comedian was born in 1961 and played a dim-witted barman in the comedy series Cheers?

2 Maryam d'Abo was born in 1960 and starred in the Bond film The Living Daylights. Who played Bond in that film?

3 By what stage name was Frankenstein actor William Henry Pratt, who died in February 1969, better known?

4 Which 1969-born actor starred in Robin Hood Prince of Thieves, Broken Arrow, True Romance, and the TV series Mr Robot?

5 Which of these 1969 films DIDN'T feature Clint Eastwood? Midnight Cowboy, Where Eagles Dare or Paint Your Wagon?

6 Which British comedy series, debuting in 1968 and running until 1977, was originally called The Fighting Tigers?

7 What nationality was philosopher, author and journalist Albert Camus, who died in January 1960?

8 David Bowie changed his surname (to Bowie) in 1966, from what, to avoid confusion with a member of the Monkees?

9 Which American singer and actress was born in New York in 1963, crowned Miss America in 1984 and had leading roles in both Desperate Housewives and Ugly Betty?

10 What did singer Jim Reeves crash, resulting in his death, in August 1964? A motorbike, a car, a hovercraft or an aircraft?

Quiz 41

1 Which airline started to fly the world's first 737 aircraft in 1968? Emirates, Lufthansa or Qantas?

2 Which British actor, born in 1967, played Obergruppenfuhrer John Smith in Amazon's The Man

in the High Castle, and also appeared in the TV series' Middlemarch and The Pillars of the Earth?

3 Which Scottish classical singer, who found fame singing I Dreamed a Dream on Britain's Got Talent, was born on 1 April 1961?

4 When Hawaii became part of the US on 4 July 1960, how many states in total did the US have? 50, 51 or 52?

5 Who was the author of The Grapes of Wrath, Of Mice and Men and East of Eden, who died in New York on 20 December 1968?

6 In which year were Rubber Ball by Bobby Vee, I Want to be Wanted by Brenda Lee and It's Now or Never by Elvis all released? 1960, 1961 or 1962?

7 Which all-female group had a hit with Stop In The Name of Love in 1965?

8 Which Scottish racing driver won both the Indianapolis 500 and the Formula One world driving championship in 1965?

9 Which British singer was born in June 1960 and went on to front the group Simply Red?

10 What was the profession of Ross Geller, played by 1966-born David Schwimmer in the TV series Friends?

Quiz 42

1 Which 1963-born actress played Phoebe in the TV series Friends?

2 Which Alabama-born singer and jazz pianist died in 1965 after having hits with Get Your Kicks on Route 66, Unforgettable and Nature Boy?

3 Who was the very first Bond girl, appearing in 1962's Dr No?

4 Which painting was valued at US$100m in November 1962 before going on a tour of the United States? Van Gogh's Sunflowers, Edvard Munch's The Scream, or Da Vinci's Mona Lisa?

5   Which LHO was an assassin who never made it to trial?

6   In which part of the United Kingdom did 'The Troubles' first manifest in the mid-1960s?

7   What was the top speed of the Jaguar E-Type, launched on 3 April 1961? 100mph, 150mph or 180mph?

8   Name the rock band fronted by 1962-born Axl Rose.

9   Which actor was born in 1968 and went on to star in The Fresh Prince of Bel-Air, Men in Black and Wild Wild West?

10 Peter Sellers starred in both Dr Strangelove and The Pink Panther, each released in the 1960s. Which came first?

Quiz 43

1   Which country hosted the 1966 FIFA World Cup?

2   Which two words did Swiss-born architect and designer Charles-Edouard Jeanneret, who died in 1965, choose in place of his birth name?

3   Which birthday did Elvis celebrate in 1965? 25, 30 or 35?

4   Which popular fast food item, introduced in 1967, was originally called The Aristocrat, and the Blue Ribbon Burger, before getting its present name?

5   What was the top-grossing film of 1961? The Guns of Navarone, The Parent Trap or West Side Story?

6   What was the name of the "boyfriend" of the Barbie doll, introduced in 1961?

7   Which actor, born in Chicago in 1966, featured in the two Back to the Future films, as well as Dead Calm and Titanic?

8   Whose 1966 book, In Cold Blood, told the story of the real life 1959 murder of the Clutter family in Holcomb, Kansas?

9   Who was elected president of the Palestine Liberation Organisation, in Egypt, in February 1969?

10 Which of the Desperate Housewives actors played Lois Lane opposite 1966-born Dean Cain in the series Lois & Clark: The New Adventures of Superman?

Quiz 44

1   At which US car maker's British plant did sewing machinists go on strike in 1968, demanding equal pay for women? The story of the strike was later made into a film called Made in Dagenham.

2   Who did Brazil beat to win the 1962 FIFA World Cup? Czechoslovakia, Romania or Bulgaria?

3   Which country launched its first nuclear submarine, Dreadnought, in October 1960? The United Kingdom, France or China?

4   Which British comedian who later starred in Fawlty Towers and A Fish Called Wanda, had his cinema debut in 1968's Interlude?

5   From whom did Lucille Ball file for divorce in March 1960 after 19 years of marriage?

6   Who wrote the music and lyrics of The Sound of Music?

7   Which American actor, who died aged 60 in 1961, acted in A Farewell to Arms, For Whom The Bell Tolls and High Noon?

8   What is the stage name of 1965-born musician Saul Hudson, a founding member of the band Guns N Roses?

9   Whose song, Be My Baby, was the fifth highest grossing single of 1963?

10 James Bond author Ian Fleming released two books in 1964. One was You Only Live Twice. What was the other?

Quiz 45

1   Rearrange "Widest Oysters" to find the name of a New York musical.

2   Which actress, who died in London, aged 53, in 1967, won Oscars for playing Scarlett O'Hara in Gone with the Wind, and Blanche DuBois in A Streetcar Named Desire?

3   Which European country detonated its first nuclear bomb in February 1960? France, Germany or the United Kingdom?

4   Which British singer was born in December 1960 and had a hit with Kids in America in 1981?

5   How old was Martin Luther King Jr when he was assassinated in April 1968? 29, 39 or 49?

6   Over which natural phenomena did the Skylon Tower first open for visitors in 1965? Grand Canyon, Great Barrier Reef or Niagara Falls?

7   Whose song, A Whiter Shade of Pale, was the biggest hit single of 1967?

8   Which British actor, who would later play Queen Elizabeth II, and the TV detective Jane Tennison, made her cinema debut in 1966 in the film Press for Time?

9   Which TRB was a duo who had hits including You've Lost that Lovin' Feeling and Unchained Melody?

10 Name the 1962-born singer who recorded the album Tuesday Night Music Club, and the theme to the James Bond film Tomorrow Never Dies.

Quiz 46

1   Which British singer reached the top of the US charts with her 1965 release, Downtown?

2   In which year was the Compact Cassette introduced? 1962, 1964, 1966 or 1968?

3   Who played Inspector Clouseau in the 1963 film The Pink Panther?

4   The first volume of which American writer and poet's autobiography was 1969's I Know Why the Caged Bird Sings?

5   Which Roald Dahl book was first published in January 1964? Charlie and the Chocolate Factory, Fantastic Mr Fox or The BFG?

6   In which 1968 science fiction film did Leonard Rossiter play Dr Andrei Smyslov?

7   Which future president was arrested in 1962 and would go on to serve a prison term of 27 years?

8   Who delivered a 1963 speech before 250,000 people from the steps of the Lincoln Memorial in Washington DC in which he coined the phrase "I Have a Dream"?

9   Which British singer, born in 1966, is best known for the song Never Gonna Give You Up?

10   Which country opened its first legal casino in 1962? Australia, Canada or Britain?

Quiz 47

1   What was the nationality of 1960-born racing driver Ayrton Senna? Argentinian, Brazilian or Portuguese?

2   Who did Yale University announce that it was going to admit for the first time in November 1968? Non-white students, women or overseas applicants?

3   How many audio tracks could be stored on the tape format introduced in 1964? 8, 12 or 16?

4   Which American car manufacturer launched the Cortina in the United Kingdom in September 1962?

5   Corgi Toys introduced the best selling model car of all time in 1965. Was it James Bond's Aston Martin DB5, Lady Penelope's pink Rolls Royce, Chitty Chitty Bang Bang, or The Saint's Volvo P1800?

6   What is the professional name of the 1960-born Belgian actor known as "The Muscles from Brussels"?

7   By which name was the novelist Nevil Norway, who died in January 1960, better known?

8   Having been turned down by Tony Bennet, who had a 1968 number one hit with What a Wonderful World?

9   Which Beatles album includes the tracks Lucy in the Sky With Diamonds, With a Little Help from my Friends and When I'm Sixty-Four?

10 American involvement in which war officially began on 11 December 1961? Vietnam, Korea or the Gulf war?

Quiz 48

1   Which country did 1968-born Celine Dion represent in the Eurovision Song Contest of 1988? France, Belgium or Switzerland?

2   The state funeral of which wartime leader took place on 30 January 1965? Winston Churchill, Charles de Gaulle or Harry Truman?

3   A 2003 poll put the line "You're only supposed to blow the bloody doors off!" top of a list of the best movie one-liners ever. Which 1969 film was it taken from?

4   Which European country launched its first TV station on 23 February 1966? Greece, Poland or Romania?

5   What was the name of Audrey Hepburn's character in 1961's Breakfast at Tiffany's? Tiffany, Audrey or Holly?

6   Which 1967 film starring Telly Savalas, Charles Bronson and Donald Sutherland, was based on a novel inspired by a group called the Filthy Thirteen?

7   Which 1969 movie starred Paul Newman and Robert Redford playing Wyoming outlaws?

8   Which author of The Chronicles of Narnia and The Screwtape Letters died of renal failure at his home in Oxford on 22 November 1963?

9   Which group was formed in 1962 when Mick Jagger and Keith Richards met Brian Jones at The Ealing Club?

10 When sworn in on 20 January 1961, did John F Kennedy become the 30th, 33rd or 35th president of the United States?

Quiz 49

1. What was the name of the satellite that, in 1962, made the first transatlantic broadcast?

2. Which animated movie about a pack of dogs did Disney release on 25 January 1961?

3. Which actor, known for Smokey and The Bandit, and who was offered but turned down the roles of both James Bond and Han Solo, made his cinema debut in 1961's Angel Baby?

4. Golda Meir became the first female prime minister of which country in March 1969?

5. Which TV series features a crime-fighting bottlenose dolphin, and has been called an aquatic Lassie?

6. How old was civil rights movement leader Martin Luther King when he became the youngest ever recipient of the Nobel Peace Prize in 1964? 30, 35 or 40?

7. Which American actor, who starred in The Shawshank Redemption, Driving Miss Daisy and Robin Hood Prince of Thieves, made his cinema debut in 1964 film The Pawnbroker?

8. After 19 years' work, the Mont Blanc tunnel opened in 1965 between Switzerland and which of its neighbours? Italy, France or Germany?

9. Which historical movie starring Elizabeth Taylor and Richard Burton was the highest-grossing film of 1963?

10. Following almost three decades as presenter of Top Gear, what was the name of the show that 1960-born presenter Jeremy Clarkson went on to front for Amazon?

Quiz 50

1. Which French politician was born in August 1968 and took over from her father as leader of the Front National party?

2 Name the Dickens book about London pickpockets that was made into a film in 1968.

3 Which future husband and wife began singing together in 1964 as Caesar and Cleo?

4 What nationality is 1962-born actor Jim Carrey? American, Australian or Canadian?

5 Which musician was not seen in public for more than a year after injuring himself in a 1966 motorcycle accident near his home in Woodstock, New York?

6 What nationality is Brigitte Nielsen, the model and actress born in 1963, who was married to Sylvester Stallone for two years from 1985? Swedish, Norwegian or Danish?

7 Plans to build which New York structure were announced in January 1964? The World Trade Center (Twin Towers), The Empire State Building or the Chrysler Building?

8 Name the actor, born in 1964, who Starred in Miss Congeniality, The Proposal, Crash and Two Weeks Notice.

9 Which groundbreaking Warren Beatty film of 1967 marked Gene Wilder's cinematic debut?

10 In which country did student Jan Palach set himself on fire to protest its Soviet invasion?

Quiz 51

1 Which 1969-born actor is the son of Downton Abbey's Dame Maggie Smith and played villain Gustav Graves in the 2002 James Bond film, Die Another Day?

2 Which 1968-born actor played Arnold Jackson from 1978 until 1986 in the TV series Diff'rent Strokes?

3 Which Northern Irish actor known for Cold Feet, Waking Ned and Murphy's Law, was born in County Antrim in 1965?

4 Which aircraft made its maiden flight on 9 February 1969 from its manufacturer's airfield outside Seattle? Concorde, Boeing 747 or the Mig fighter jet?

5   Which 1980s film featured the US Navy Fighter Weapons School at Miramar, which had been established in March 1969?

6   Which British prime minister, who took over from Winston Churchill immediately after the Second World War, died in 1967? Clement Attlee, Neville Chamberlain or Anthony Eden?

7   Which film star, born in the 1960s and later starring in The Godfather and Single White Female, is an anagram of "Forged Bandit"?

8   What did McDonald's restaurants start selling for the first time in 1967? Happy Meals, Chicken Nuggets or Big Macs?

9   The Beatles performed for the first time at which iconic Liverpool club on 9 February 1961?

10 Marcia Cross and Felicity Huffman were both born in 1962, and both starred in Desperate Housewives. Which is older?

Quiz 52

1   For which album cover did Peter Blake and Jann Haworth create a collage of over 70 people and a range of musical instruments?

2   In which year did Mao initiate China's Cultural Revolution? 1966, 1967 or 1968?

3   In which city was the heist, central to the 1969 film The Italian Job, staged? Rome, Milan or Turin?

4   What was the global population at the start of the 1960s? Three, four or five billion?

5   Which clothing store opened its first branch ever in San Francisco in August 1969? Primark, TK Maxx or Gap?

6   With which country did the United States sever relations in 1961, and not restore them until 2015?

7   Whose famous recording of "Non, Je Ne Regrette Rien" was released in France in December 1960?

8   Which New York born actor who appeared in the three Godfather films, as well as Scent of a Woman, Donnie Brasco and Carlito's Way, first appeared in cinemas in 1969 in the film Me, Natalie?

9   Who released the legendary Pet Sounds album in 1966?

10   Which company introduced Tab, its first diet drink, on 1 May 1963?

Quiz 53

1   Which artist married a member of The Beatles in Gibraltar in 1969?

2   Was John F Kennedy, winner of the 1960 US presidential election, running for the Republican or Democratic party?

3   Which iconic lighting product was invented by a British accountant in 1963?

4   Which surreal comedy programme starring John Cleese, Terry Gilliam, Eric Idle, Michael Palin and a dead parrot aired for the first time in October 1969?

5   In which country did construction of the Aswan High Dam begin in January 1960? Egypt, Iran or Libya?

6   On which day of the week did the 1960s begin?

7   Which US TV show of the mid-1960s featured Robert Vaughn and David McCallum battling adversaries from an organisation called THRUSH?

8   What was invented at Xerox in 1969? The computer mouse, the laser printer or the photocopier?

9   What was the role of Dag Hammarskjold, who died in an air crash en route to Congo in 1961?

10   Which Scottish actor, born in April 1961, appeared in Trainspotting, the Full Monty and Angela's Ashes, and played the villain in James Bond film The World is Not Enough?

Quiz 54

1 Two groups released the song Ob-La-Di, Ob-La-Da in 1968. One was The Marmalade, who took it to number one. Who was the other?

2 Which British singer released Anyone Who Had a Heart in 1964?

3 What was the name of the home help played by 1961-born Jane Leeves in the TV sitcom Frasier?

4 What came first? The Sound of Music or Mary Poppins?

5 Who is the 1961-born New Zealand director of the Lord of the Rings film trilogy and The Hobbit?

6 Which two countries set up a hotline allowing their leaders to communicate directly in June 1963?

7 Which Andrew Lloyd Webber musical was performed for the first time on 1 March 1968? Evita, Cats or Joseph and the Amazing Technicolor Dreamcoat?

8 In which month of 1965 did India and Pakistan go to war: July, August or September?

9 After which farmyard animal was the Cuban bay that US forces tried, unsuccessfully, to raid in 1961, named?

10 Richard Burton and Elizabeth Taylor married twice. The second time was 1975. When was the first?

Quiz 55

1 Who played the title role of the TV series Ironside?

2 Was Spartacus, from the 1960 film of the same name, a Roman or Greek slave?

3 Who wrote the book, To Kill a Mockingbird, which was turned into a 1962 film starring Gregory Peck?

4 Who released the album That's Life in 1966? Frank Sinatra, Sammy Davis or Roy Orbison?

5   Which 1968 film included the songs Food, Glorious Food; Consider Yourself; and You've Got to Pick a Pocket or Two?

6   What was the name of the fugitive in the 1963 – 67 TV series, The Fugitive? Kimble, Thimble or Dimble?

7   Which actor, born in Kentucky in 1963, dated Vanessa Paradis between 1998 and 2012, and starred in the Pirates of the Caribbean film series?

8   Was the sentient computer that ran the deep space ship 1968's 2001: A Space Odyssey called Hal, Sal or Mal?

9   How old was 1961-born Princess Diana when she died in a Paris car crash?

10 Which British actor, born in Lancashire in 1964, went on to play the ninth incarnation of Time Lord Doctor Who when the BBC revived the sci-fi series in 2004?

Quiz 56

1   Which of these 1969 movies starred Clint Eastwood: Easy Rider, Butch Cassidy and the Sundance Kid, Midnight Cowboy or Paint Your Wagon?

2   Which British designer, born in February 1967, is credited with inventing the iMac, iPhone and iPad for Apple?

3   Which Beatles album included the tracks Ticket To Ride and Yesterday?

4   Which Anglo-French novelist, best known for her book Chocolat, was born in Yorkshire, England, in July 1964?

5   Where did the Flintstones live? Rockhampton, Stoneville or Bedrock?

6   Which Canadian singer songwriter was born in 1961 and is known for the song Constant Craving?

7   Which musician's name is an anagram of "Bland Boy"?

8   Where did Russian ballet dancer Rudolf Nureyev request asylum while on tour with the Kirov Ballet on 16 June 1961? London, Paris or New York?

9   Which German tennis player, born in 1969, was ranked world number one during her career and won 22 Grand Slam titles?

10 True or false: the first Mini was produced in the 1960s?

Quiz 57

1   Which country gained control of the Gaza Strip and Golan Heights at the end of 1967's Six Days War?

2   Which LCL, a book published by Penguin, was the subject of a notorious obscenity trial?

3   In which country was Gladiator actor Russell Crowe born in 1964? Australia, New Zealand or Singapore?

4   Who employed a butler called Aloysius Parker in the TV series Thunderbirds?

5   Which former US president, who served throughout the Great Depression and commissioned a dam on the Colorado River that now bears his name, died in October 1964?

6   Which film was Walt Disney producing when he died in December 1966? Snow White, Fantasia or Jungle Book?

7   In which city was John F Kennedy assassinated in November 1963?

8   Unscramble the anagram "Insolent Thefts" to find the title of a long-running cartoon series.

9   Which former US first lady, who lived at the White House from 1933 until 1945, died in November 1962?

10 Which singer had her cinema acting debut in the 1968 film Funny Girl?

Quiz 58

1   Which actor, known for Speed, Point Break, The Matrix and others, was born in Beirut, Lebanon, in September 1964?

2 Which American actress, born in December 1964, played both Lois Lane in The New Adventures of Superman, and Susan Mayer in Desperate Housewives?

3 Whose debut album of 1967 included the track Light My Fire?

4 Who was the manager of The Beatles, who died in 1967, aged 32, following an accidental overdose?

5 Name the lead singer of Australian band INXS who was born in January 1960 and died aged 37 in November 1997.

6 Which American singer-songwriter, known for hits like Fast Car and Talkin' 'bout a Revolution, was born in Ohio in March 1964?

7 How tall is the steel Gateway Arch completed in St Louis in October 1965? 630ft (190m), 730ft (222m) or 830ft (252m)?

8 Name the German racing driver who was born in 1969 and won 91 Grand Prix races, 68 pole positions and clocked the fastest lap 77 times in his career.

9 What did Pope Paul VI publish a letter condemning in July 1968? The Vietnam War, pop music or birth control?

10 Which Audrey Hepburn musical of 1964 was based on the George Bernard Shaw stage play, Pygmalion?

Quiz 59

1 Which American novelist, who wrote standing up, won the Nobel Prize for Literature in 1954, published The Old Man and The Sea, For Whom The Bell Tolls, and The Sun Also Rises, before committing suicide in 1961?

2 Which character, created by PL Travers, was the subject of a Disney film released in 1964?

3 Which model, born in 1965 and married for some time to Andre Agassi, starred in the films Blue Lagoon and Endless Love?

4   Which SK directed 2001: A Space Odyssey and Dr Strangelove?

5   Which two countries signed the 1963 Elysee Treaty, which ended centuries of rivalry between them? Britain and France, France and Germany, or Germany and Russia?

6   Name the American actor, born in 1965, who took the lead role in 1992 film Chaplin, was Calista Flockhart's love interest in Ally McBeal and, in 2008, began playing Iron Man in Marvel films?

7   Where was Robert F Kennedy when he was assassinated in June 1968? A hotel, an airport or an office building?

8   Was George Clooney born in 1961, 1964 or 1967?

9   Of the four men who served as US president during the 60s – Eisenhower, Kennedy, Johnson and Nixon – who was the oldest when he came to power?

10 Which city officially took over from New York as the largest in the world in 1965? Beijing, Seoul or Tokyo?

Quiz 60

1   Which country found 40 microphones embedded in the walls of its Moscow embassy in May 1964? The United States, the United Kingdom or France?

2   Which rights activist was assassinated in February 1965?

3   Which British-Canadian actor, born in 1966, went on to play Jack Bauer in the '24' series of TV shows?

4   Which child star who later featured in Judgement at Nuremberg and The Wizard of Oz, died of an unintended overdose in 1969?

5   Where would you find a picture that included, among other people, Bob Dylan, Fred Astaire, Mae West, Edgar Allan Poe, Marilyn Monroe, Tony Curtis and Karl Marx?

6   In which country were the Winter Olympic Games of 1968 held? France, Italy or Switzerland?

7   Of which country was Josip Broz Tito named president for life in April 1963? Bulgaria, Romania or Yugoslavia?

8   In March 1967, who became the first pop stars to go on display at London's Madame Tussauds Wax Museum?

9   What, in 1967, became the first English-language song to win the Eurovision Song Contest? Congratulations by Cliff Richard, Puppet on a String by Sandie Shaw or Boom Bang a Bang by Lulu?

10   Which computer processor manufacturer was founded in Silicon Valley in 1968 by Gordon Moore and Robert Noyce?

Quiz 61

1   Which member of the Osmonds was born in 1963 and became the youngest performer to have a number 1 single in the UK with Long Haired Lover from Liverpool in 1972?

2   Which American police serial, which ran from 1968 until 1980, frequently ended with the line "Book 'em Danno!"?

3   What was the profession of Perry Mason, the titular character in the nine-season drama serial that came to an end in 1966?

4   Who played James Bond in the 1965 film Thunderball?

5   Which September 1960-born British actor achieved international success in Four Weddings and a Funeral, Notting Hill and Love Actually?

6   Regular hovercraft services started between France and England in 1966. Competition from which alternative route between the countries saw them terminated in 2000?

7   Which duo released The Sound of Silence in 1965?

8   Who crashed his motorbike while attempting to jump 141 feet over the Las Vegas fountains at Caesars Palace in December 1967?

9   Of which country was Indira Gandhi elected prime minister in January 1966?

10   Which author of Cannery Row, The Grapes of Wrath and Of Mice and Men, won the Nobel Prize for Literature in 1962?

Quiz 62

1   In which city was Robert F Kennedy assassinated in June 1968? New York, Dallas or Los Angeles?

2   In which country was Jane Leeves, known for playing home help Daphne Moon in Frasier, born? Canada, Australia or the United Kingdom

3   In which city was Jimi Hendrix jailed after trashing a hotel room in January 1968? Stockholm, Helsinki or Oslo?

4   Midnight Cowboy and The Graduate were released in the 1960s and both starred Dustin Hoffman. Which came first?

5   Which AYLT was the title of an Elvis hit of 1960?

6   The BBC's Time Lord, Doctor Who, regenerated for the first time ever in October 1966 when William Hartnell transformed into... who?

7   Where was The House of the Rising Sun in the 1964 song of the same name?

8   Which British singer's real name was Priscilla Maria Veronica White?

9   How did religious leader Giovanni Battista Montini come to the world's attention in June 1963?

10   Which US singer was born Heidi Stern in September 1960 and went on to record The Power of Love?

Quiz 63

1   What is the name of the oversized film format, that makes larger than normal cinema screens possible, which was first introduced in 1967?

2   Who played James Bond for the first time in 1962?

3   Which landmass became the 50th state of the United States on US Independence Day 1960?

4   Who directed the 1968 film, 2001: A Space Odyssey?

5   Which British artist, famed for his shark in formaldehyde and sawing a cow in half, was born in Bristol in 1965?

6   In March 1964, sales of The Beatles music made up what proportion of the US singles market? 10%, 30% or 60%?

7   Of which Bond girl's name is "Lousy Grapes" an anagram?

8   Which actor was elected Governor of California in November 1966?

9   Name the 1962-born Australian naturalist, nicknamed The Crocodile Hunter, who was killed by a stingray barb in 2006.

10   Name the British singer songwriter and front-man of the group Blur who was born in London in March 1968.

Quiz 64

1   Which member of the Jackson singing family was born in Indiana in 1966 and is known for the songs Rhythm Nation and That's the Way Love Goes?

2   Name the 1969-born Australian actress who starred in Elizabeth: The Golden Age, Peter Jackson's Lord of the Rings trilogy and The Talented Mr Ripley.

3   Who played British NATO spy John Drake in a series called Danger Man in the UK, Secret Agent in the US, and either Destination Danger or John Drake in other countries, between 1960 and 1968?

4   How many Academy Awards did the 1961 film West Side Story win? Five, 10 or 15?

5   Which Frank Herbert sci-fi epic, published in 1965, is set on a planet which is the only known source of Spice, the most valuable substance in the universe?

6   Who broke new ground when they toured the first ever rock opera, Tommy, in 1965?

7   Which BOP was the site of an unsuccessful American invasion of Cuba?

8   The first live television broadcast from where occurred on 14 October 1968? A submarine, an aeroplane or a spacecraft?

9   Which Texan, born in 1965, went on to found a computer firm named after himself whose products are found in offices worldwide?

10   Which 1969 novel by Mario Puzo tells the story of a fictional New York mafia family headed by Vito Corleone, which was later filmed starring Marlon Brando and Al Pacino?

Quiz 65

1   Which Julia, the 27th prime minister of Australia, was born on 29 September 1961?

2   Which Hanna-Barbera cartoon about a feline that lived in a dustbin ran from September 1961 until April 1962?

3   How old was Sean Connery in 1962 when he first played James Bond? 22, 28, 32 or 38?

4   Which TPP was a rose coloured diamond in a series of Peter Sellers films?

5   True or false: the Soviet Union launched a single satellite containing two dogs, 40 mice, two rats and a variety of plants in August 1960.

6   Which sitcom, debuting in 1964, depicted a family of monsters living in Mockingbird Heights, California?

7   Who became the first American in space on 5 May 1961?

8   Rearrange the letters in "Owner Investor" to find the name of an Elvis Presley song.

9   Who was sworn in as the 37th president of the United States in January 1969?

10   Which actress, who featured in Splash, Blade Runner and Wall Street, was born in December 1960?

Quiz 66

1 Which scientist, who died in 1967, is often called the "father of the atomic bomb" for his role in the Manhattan Project to develop a nuclear weapon during the Second World War?

2 Which American composer and songwriter known for songs such as I Get a Kick out of You and I've Got You Under my Skin, died in October 1964?

3 Who did John F Kennedy beat to win the 1960 US presidential election?

4 Which country introduced the world's first approved oral contraceptive pill in May 1960? Switzerland, France or the United States?

5 Which MPFC was a comedy series remembered for its sketch about a dead parrot?

6 What is Unix, invented in summer 1969?

7 The Beatles released their seventh studio album in August 1966. Was it Revolver, Help or Rubber Soul?

8 Which 1967-born British actor starred in Pirates of the Caribbean, Gosford Park and Enigma, and took the lead role in BBC comedy Rev?

9 Which central American country hosted the 1968 Summer Olympics?

10 Brazil moved its capital to the newly-built Brasilia in April 1960. Where had it been previously?

Quiz 67

1 Patrick McGoohan's character in the 1960s TV series The Prisoner was known only by a number. Which one? Number One, Number Three or Number Six?

2 Which novel by Boris Pasternak was filmed by David Lean, with Julie Christie and Omar Sharif in lead roles, in 1965?

3   How old was Che Guevara when he was assassinated in 1967? 39, 49 or 59?

4   Which 1962-born actress was married to Bruce Willis from 1987 until 2000?

5   The first ever televised royal marriage occurred in May 1960. Which royal family was involved? British, Swedish or Japanese?

6   Which 1969 film starred Dennis Hopper and Henry Fonda as a pair of motorcyclists travelling through the southern US?

7   Which actor, born in 1935 and known for films such as The Dirty Dozen, Kelly's Heroes and Eye of the Needle first appeared in 1963 in the film The World Ten Times Over?

8   Which British comedian, born in 1961, found fame with The Office and Extras, but got his first taste of public performance in the group Seona Dancing?

9   Which American actor, who found fame in Fantastic Voyage and One Million Years BC, first appeared on the big screen in 1964, in A House is Not a Home?

10   Who led China's Cultural Revolution of 1966 - 1967?

Quiz 68

1   Whose 1966 album was called Pet Sounds?

2   What was the top grossing film of 1969? Midnight Cowboy, On Her Majesty's Secret Service or Butch Cassidy and the Sundance Kid?

3   What was the B-side to The Beatles' 1966 hit, We Can Work it Out? Paperback Writer, Eleanor Rigby or Day Tripper?

4   Which 1964 book introduced the character of Caractacus Potts, who spends his time buying and renovating old cars?

5   Which member of The Beatles' original line-up died in Hamburg in 1962?

6   In which year did Ford introduce the iconic Mustang car? 1964, 1966 or 1968?

7   Name the US silent film star, nicknamed The Great Stone
     Face on account of performing impressive slapstick in a
     deadpan manner, who died in 1966.

8   Which French footballer was born in 1966 and played
     for Marseilles, Montpellier, Nimes, Bordeaux, Leeds and
     Manchester United among other teams?

9   Which band's name is an anagram of "Parlour Chum"?

10   Where was the TV series Ironside set? New York, Los
     Angeles or San Francisco?

Quiz 69

1   Which country ran its last ever scheduled passenger steam
     train in August 1968? The United Kingdom, United States,
     China or the Soviet Union?

2   Who was the Irish playwright and novelist, author of
     Waiting for Godot, among others, who won the Nobel Prize
     for Literature in 1969?

3   What was the profession of Belgian Georges Lemaitre who
     was the first to suggest that the universe started with a Big
     Bang, and who died in June 1966?

4   Which 1960-born actress won a BAFTA award for Best
     Supporting Actress for her work in Four Weddings and a
     Funeral, and an Academy Award nomination for The English
     Patient?

5   English novelist Helen Fielding was born in February 1960.
     Name the female diarist she created in newspapers and,
     later, novels and films.

6   Which 1967 comedy film starring Dustin Hoffman told the
     story of a 21 year old being seduced by an older woman?

7   Of which country did Nicolae Ceausescu become leader in
     1965? Albania, Romania or Bulgaria?

8   In which film did Clarke Gable, who died in November 1960,
     have the line "Frankly, my dear, I don't give a damn"?

9 Which MQ invented the miniskirt?

10 Which 1961-born actor found fame while playing Dr Doug Ross in TV medical drama ER?

Quiz 70

1 For what right did Sylvia Pankhurst spend much of her life campaigning before her death in 1960?

2 Who played Butch Cassidy in 1969's Butch Cassidy and the Sundance Kid? Paul Newman or Robert Redford?

3 How many singles did The Beatles release in 1964? 1, 9 or 19?

4 Where was Checkpoint Charlie, at which American and Soviet troops had a stand-off on 27 October 1961?

5 Which female actor's name is an anagram of "Injured Wales"?

6 Which country surrendered Goa to India in 1961 after ruling it for 400 years? The United Kingdom, France or Portugal?

7 Which future princess and heir to the British throne, was born on 1 July 1961?

8 Which CMZ led China through the Cultural Revolution?

9 Which country's first national television station, RTE, went on air on 31 December 1961? Ireland, Iceland or Greenland?

10 Name the rock opera about a blind boy who played pinball machines, recorded by The Who in 1965.

Quiz 71

1 Who won the 1962 Best Actor Oscar for playing Atticus Finch in To Kill a Mocking Bird? Gregory Peck, Burt Reynolds or George Peppard?

2 True or false: Star Trek's Leonard Nimoy also starred in Mission: Impossible.

3 Who played Maria von Trapp in the 1965 film The Sound of Music?

4 Name the 1960-born film director responsible for Twin Peaks.

5 Which TV show, running from 1964 until 1968, featured the exploits of secret agents working for the United Network Command for Law and Enforcement?

6 The first James Bond film was released in 1962. What was it called?

7 In which city was the Motown Record Corporation founded in 1960?

8 What is the middle name of 1961-born Michael J Fox? Andrew, Anthony or Arnold?

9 What was the highest-grossing film of the 1960s? Mary Poppins, The Sound of Music, 2001: A Space Odyssey or The Italian Job?

10 Which British former presenter of Top Gear, who went on to present Amazon's The Grand Tour, was born in Bristol in January 1963?

Quiz 72

1 Name the singer songwriter born in Turin in 1967, who married French president Nicolas Sarkozy in 2008.

2 Which civil rights activist was assassinated in April 1968?

3 In which US city did Timothy McVeigh, who was born in 1968, destroy the Alfred P Murrah Federal Building in 1995?

4 Of which country did Willy Brandt become leader on 21 October 1969? Austria, East Germany or West Germany?

5 What was Flipper, in the TV series of the same name?

6 What is the Pink Panther, which features on the film series bearing that name?

7 Which 1964-born French actress turned down roles in both Jurassic Park and Schindler's List but took the lead role in the 2000 film, Chocolat?

8   Which jazz vocalist, who topped the charts in 1991 with I Wonder Why, was born in Idaho in 1965?

9   What is the real name of the 1965-born British author who sometimes writes books as Robert Galbraith?

10   Who was the author of The African Queen, and the Horatio Hornblower novels, who died in 1966? CS Forester, CS Lewis or GK Chesterton?

Quiz 73

1   Which city opened its Olympiaturm in 1968, in advance of its hosting the Summer Olympic Games four years later? Munich, Berlin or Cologne?

2   Which 1960-born singer had a daughter in 1996 called Heavenly Hiraani Tiger Lily?

3   Who was found guilty on 14 March 1964 of killing Kennedy assassin Lee Harvey Oswald?

4   When did The Beatles first visit America? 1963, 64 or 65?

5   Who played Spock in the original series of Star Trek, which debuted in 1966?

6   Who played James Bond for the one and only time in 1969's On Her Majesty's Secret Service?

7   Rearrange "Tidal Forces" to spell the name of a revolutionary leader.

8   Which Apollo mission first put humans on the moon? 9, 11 or 13?

9   David Duchovny was born in August 1960 and went on to play which character in The X Files?

10   What was the name of the witch, played by Elizabeth Montgomery in the TV series Bewitched? Samantha, Tabatha or Agatha?

Quiz 74

1   What was the codename of the long-range, high-altitude spy plane capable of flying at three times the speed of sound that the US put into service in December 1966?

2   What was the Love Bug that starred in the 1968 Disney film of the same name?

3   What was the job title of Dana Scully, the character played by 1968-born actor Gillian Anderson in The X-Files?

4   Whose body was moved to a permanent burial place in Arlington National Cemetery in March 1967?

5   Which Canadian actor, born in January 1962, went on to star in The Truman Show and Ace Ventura, Pet Detective?

6   Which green-skinned, muscular, humanoid superhero was introduced in May 1962?

7   What TFF was space, according to the opening monologue of Star Trek?

8   Rearrange the letters in "Startle" to spell the name of the first television satellite.

9   Which former lead from The Avengers was the Bond Girl in 1969's On Her Majesty's Secret Service?

10 True or false: until July 1969 the US had $10,000 bills in circulation.

Quiz 75

1   Which car manufacturing firm was established in Italy in October 1963? Fiat, Alfa Romeo or Lamborghini?

2   How far below the buttocks does a true mini skirt fall? No more than 5cm, 10cm or 15cm?

3   Which pop singer starred in the 1963 film, Summer Holiday, about a group of friends who convert a double decker bus into a holiday caravan?

4 Why did the Texas School Book Depository come to international attention in November 1963?

5 Which company invented the Compact Cassette, and released it to the world in 1962? Philips, Sony or Apple?

6 Which country launched Ariel 3 in 1967, being the first satellite ever developed outside the Soviet Union or United States? Was it China, India or the United Kingdom?

7 What change was made to the US flag between the beginning and end of 1960?

8 Who played Captain von Trapp in 1965's The Sound of Music?

9 What was the maiden name of Paul McCartney's wife Linda before the pair married in March 1969?

10 How many people walked on the moon in the 1960s? Two, four, six or eight?

Quiz 76

1 Which 1967 animation featured Baloo, Bagheera, King Louie and Shere Khan?

2 Which two countries have taken over the majority of the United States in Philip K Dick's 1962 novel The Man in the High Castle? Choose from Germany, China, Russia and Japan.

3 How many number 1 hits did The Supremes release between 1964 and 1969? 3, 6, 9 or 12?

4 Catch-22, the title of Joseph Heller's 1961 book, has been adopted in everyday language to describe a no-win situation. What was the book originally called? Catch-8, Catch-18 or Catch-88?

5 Who wrote Brideshead Revisited, and Decline and Fall, and died in April 1966 aged 62?

6 Which everyday television feature was seen for the first time during the 1960 Presidential debates between John F

Kennedy and Richard Nixon? Colour pictures, subtitles or split screen?

7   By what name is the 1960-born singer-songwriter Paul David Hewson better known?

8   Who beat Barry Goldwater in the 1964 US election to remain president for another term?

9   Name the English filmmaker, born in 1968, known for the films Lock Stock and Two Smoking Barrels, Snatch and Revolver, and for being married to Madonna.

10 What kind of aircraft was Francis Gary Powers flying in when shot down by a Soviet surface-to-air missile and captured?

Quiz 77

1   What was the name of Ira Levin's 1967-published second book, which centred on a young woman whose baby turns out to be the Antichrist?

2   Accounting for leap years, which decade was the longest: the 1950s, 1960s or 1970s?

3   Which heir to the British throne was born in Buckingham Palace in February 1960? Princess Anne, Prince Edward or Prince Andrew?

4   Stanley Kubrick directed Spartacus, Dr Strangelove and 2001: A Space Odyssey in the 1960s. Which came first?

5   In which country did Muammar Gaddafi overthrow the monarchy and assume rule himself in 1969? Iran, Iraq or Libya?

6   Who wrote the 1969 book As I Walked Out One Midsummer Morning, a memoir and sequel to Cider With Rosie, about an epic journey on foot from the Cotswolds to Spain?

7   Who was found dead from an overdose of sleeping pills in August 1962, despite which her death was only declared 'probably' suicide?

8   Which country gave women the right to vote in 1963? Iran, Iraq or Saudi Arabia?

9   Who became an honorary citizen of the United States in April 1963? Was it Ian Fleming, John Lennon or Winston Churchill?

10   Which actor, who was famed for playing Rhett Butler in Gone with the Wind, died in November 1960?

Quiz 78

1   Which Raymond Burr TV series came first? Perry Mason or Ironside?

2   What was the last leap year of the 1960s?

3   Which international non-governmental organisation working for the environment and wilderness protection, was founded in 1961 with a panda as its logo?

4   Who was deposed as leader of the Soviet Union on 14 October 1964? Nikita Khrushchev, Leonid Brezhnev or Joseph Stalin?

5   Who was Hubert Humphrey in 1968? Vice President of the United States, Deputy Prime Minister of the United Kingdom, or Mayor of Calgary?

6   In which year did Hughes Research Laboratories demonstrate the first working laser? 1960, 1962 or 1964?

7   Which Anglo-French aircraft had its first test flight on 2 March 1969?

8   Which English novelist and aeronautical engineer died in January 1960, leaving behind the books On the Beach, and A Town Like Alice?

9   When Zakir Hussain became president of India in 1967, he was the first person of which religion to do so? Christian, Sikh or Muslim?

10   Name the singer born in Manchester in May 1967 who went on to become lead guitarist and vocalist in Oasis.

Quiz 79

1   To whom was Cynthia Powell married between 1962 and 1968? John Lennon, Paul McCartney, Ringo Starr or George Harrison?

2   Which singer, known for the songs I Just Wanna Dance With You, Give a Little Love, The Magic is There and The Way Dreams Are, was born in County Donegal, Ireland, in December 1961?

3   Who directed the 1960 film, Psycho?

4   Who was assassinated in his car in Dealey Plaza in November 1963?

5   Which UK-based group had a US number one with House of the Rising Sun in 1964?

6   Which 1960 psychological horror depicted Janet Leigh being stabbed to death in the shower?

7   Unscramble the words "Meows Unreliably" to reveal the name of a Beatles album.

8   Which racing driver, born in 1968, has been nicknamed The Flying Finn?

9   What was the name of Inspector Clouseau's boss, played by Herbert Lom, in the 1960s series of Pink Panther films?

10 In which city was The Sound of Music set?

Quiz 80

1   Which spy drama, set in a place called The Village, was first broadcast in the United Kingdom in 1967, and the following year in the US, with Patrick McGoohan taking the lead role?

2   Which Detroit-based music company was founded in 1960?

3   What nationality is 1969-born actor Javier Bardem, known for the films No Country for Old Men, Jamon Jamon, and Skyfall? Argentinian, Portuguese or Spanish?

4   In which 1964 biopic did Barbra Streisand play comedian Fanny Brice?

5   How many actors had played James Bond in the official film series before 1968-born Daniel Craig assumed the role?

6   What did president John F Kennedy commit the United States to achieving before the end of the decade at a 1962 commencement address?

7   Which country was formed in September 1963 through the merging of the Federation of Malaya and the British crown colony of Singapore?

8   Which Beatles album featured the tracks Come Together, Here Comes the Sun and Octopus's Garden?

9   Whose song, Mr Tambourine Man, was one of the biggest hits of 1965?

10   Who would go on to play Hannibal Lecter, but first appeared in cinemas in 1967's Red, White and Zero?

Quiz 81

1   Who is the British celebrity chef, born in Scotland in 1966, who went on to present Hell's Kitchen, The F Word and Kitchen Nightmares?

2   What was 1961-born princess Diana's maiden name?

3   Which long-running British TV series featuring Simon Templar debuted in 1962 and went on for 118 episodes?

4   Which GWTW included the line "Frankly, my dear, I don't give a damn"?

5   Which actor, known for his portrayal of Captain Hawkeye Pierce in the TV series M*A*S*H was first seen in cinemas in 1963 in the film Gone Are The Days?

6   Which 1962-born actor went on to play M in the James Bond films, and Voldemort in the Harry Potter series?

7   Where did Elvis Presley and Priscilla Beaulieu marry? New York, San Francisco or Las Vegas?

8   How old was 1960-born racing driver Ayrton Senna when he died at the San Marino Grand Prix?

9   Which musical, notorious for its sexual content, anti Vietnam War stance, depiction of illegal drug use and a nude scene, opened on New York's Broadway and in London's West End in 1968?

10   Which 2008 US Presidential candidate was shot down over North Vietnam in 1967 and kept as a prisoner of war for over five years?

Quiz 82

1   In which state did the first revolving restaurant in the United States open in November 1961? Hawaii, Colorado or Wyoming?

2   Which IBLB is a quote from a speech made by president Kennedy in the German capital?

3   Which 1962 book by Ken Kesey told the story of Chief Bromden's time in an Oregon psychiatric hospital?

4   What was the last of the Beatles' studio albums released in the 1960s? Let It Be, Yellow Submarine or Abbey Road?

5   In which city is the 1964 film Mary Poppins set? London, Manchester or Liverpool?

6   Which Caribbean leader was excommunicated by Pope Paul XXIII in January 1962?

7   Which fast food chain was founded on 10 June 1960? McDonalds, Domino's Pizza or Burger King?

8   Which dance, named after a soft food, became an international craze in 1962? Mashed Potato, Steamed Squash or Chilled Slush?

9   How old was 1968-born Gillian Anderson when sent the first script for The X-Files? 24, 28 or 32?

10   Which 1961 film features Audrey Hepburn singing the Oscar-winning song Moon River?

Quiz 83

1. In which 1968 movie do Jack Lemmon and Walter Matthau play two divorced men who decide to move in together even though their personalities clash?

2. Which British singer, born in 1963 and known by a single name, had a worldwide hit with the 1985 single Kiss from a Rose?

3. Which TV family featured Morticia, Gomez, Wednesday, Pugsley and Uncle Fester?

4. What is the occupation of Mary Poppins in the 1964 film of the same name?

5. Cosmonaut Yuri Gagarin was killed in what kind of crash in 1968? Plane crash, car crash or rocket crash?

6. What was discovered by a dog called Pickles, and his owner David Corbett, wrapped in newspaper in a south London garden, seven days after it had been stolen in 1966?

7. What was the name of the plaza in which President Kennedy was assassinated in 1963? Dealey, Bealey or Sealey?

8. Which star of Sex and The City did 1962-born Matthew Broderick marry in 1997?

9. In 1961, The Marvelettes was the first Motown group to get to number 1, but with which song?

10. Which 1967 musical, and its 1968 album release, featured the songs Let The Sunshine In and Aquarius?

Quiz 84

1. Whose 1964 book, Funeral in Berlin, was a follow up to his 1962 release, The IPCRESS File?

2. Who released the hit song Paint it Black in 1966? The Rolling Stones, Bob Dylan or the Yardbirds?

3   The closing ceremony of which Summer Olympic Games was the first to be transmitted around the world in colour? Mexico 1968, Tokyo 1964 or Rome 1960?

4   Who wrote Catch-22, the anti-war book published on 10 November 1961?

5   Kenneth Brannagh was born in December 1960 and went on to play which Swedish detective in the televised stories of Henning Mankell's novels?

6   How many times did Yuri Gagarin orbit Earth when he became the first human in space on 12 April 1961? Once, 10 times or 100 times?

7   Which country introduced its first decimal coins in 1968, in advance of full decimalisation three years later? China, Australia or the United Kingdom?

8   Which country won the most medals at the 1960 Summer Olympic Games? The United States, Soviet Union or host nation Italy?

9   Who played Mrs Robinson in the 1967 film, The Graduate?

10   Which TV gameshow, in which contestants are given answers for which they must formulate questions, debuted on 30 March 1964?

Quiz 85

1   On what day of the week did Neil Armstrong walk on the moon?

2   Which song, about the singer's grief on overhearing their partner is cheating, was recorded and released separately by both Marvin Gaye and Gladys Knight and the Pips?

3   Which rock band did David Gilmour join in 1968 to replace founder Syd Barrett? The Doors, Pink Floyd or The Who?

4   Which playwright, best known for the play Loot, as well as Entertaining Mr Sloane and What the Butler Saw, was murdered by his partner, Kenneth Halliwell, in 1967, aged 34?

5   In which country was the 1965 film The Sound of Music set? Germany, Austria or Bohemia?

6   Name the band fronted by 1965-born Marti Pellow that had an international hit in 1994 with Love Is All Around.

7   Who released their first single, Love Me Do, in October 1962?

8   Name the long-running sci-fi TV show created by Gene Roddenberry in 1966.

9   Which political figure did Shiran Shiran admit to killing in 1968 when he appeared in a Los Angeles court on 3 March 1974?

10   Who starred in The Lucy Show, the 1962 – 68 follow up to I Love Lucy?

Quiz 86

1   From which country did Cyprus gain independence in August 1960? Italy, Greece or the United Kingdom?

2   True or false: Gerald Ford was the last US president of the 1960s?

3   Which country changed its name to Zambia in October 1964? Biafra, Togoland or Rhodesia?

4   Which Beatles member's son, Julian, was born on 8 April 1963?

5   David Duchovny, who was born in 1960, went on to play Fox Mulder, a character who worked for which agency in The X Files?

6   According to the title of the Scott McKenzie song, what should you be sure to wear in your hair in San Francisco?

7   What was Thomasina in the 1964 Patrick McGoohan and Susan Hampshire film, The Three Lives of Thomasina?

8   For what was an Italian-American inventor called Roy Jacuzzi awarded a patent in 1968?

9   Which British actor starred in The Railway Children, An American Werewolf in London, and the TV series Call the

Midwife, but made her cinema debut in 1964 film East of Sudan?

10   In 1962, who became the first British group to reach number 1 in the US charts? The Beatles, The Shadows or The Tornados?

Quiz 87

1   Where, in 1967, was the world's first heart transplant performed? South Korea, South Sudan or South Africa?

2   Which former First Lady of the United States married Greek shipping tycoon Aristotle Onassis in October 1968?

3   Name the Welsh actress born in 1969 who starred in Entrapment, Ocean's Twelve and The Mask of Zorro, and who married Michael Douglas in 2000.

4   Which espionage television series featuring the characters John Steed and David Keel debuted on British TV in 1961?

5   Which British supergroup released its first album, The Piper at the Gates of Dawn, in 1967?

6   In front of which building in Washington DC did 50,000 protestors chant in October 1967 in an attempt to make it levitate? The White House, the Senate or the Pentagon?

7   What was being referred to in the July 1969 phrase "The Eagle has landed"?

8   In which year did the Six Days War take place? 1965, 1966 or 1967?

9   Which British author wrote the short story on which Alfred Hitchcock's 1963 film The Birds was based? Enid Blyton, Roald Dahl or Daphne du Maurier?

10   The Animals had a 1964 number one with House of the Rising Sun. Which country were they from? UK, USA or USSR?

Quiz 88

1   Who won the US presidential election of November 1960?

2   Which iconic Seattle building, visible from the apartment in the TV series Frasier, opened in April 1962?

3   Which 1965-born model was the face of Estee Lauder and appeared in the films Austin Powers International Man of Mystery, and Four Weddings and a Funeral?

4   Which 1969-born director brought us The Grand Budapest Hotel, The Royal Tenenbaums, Fantastic Mr Fox and The Darjeeling Limited?

5   Which actor, who married Annette Benning in 1992 and starred in Bonny and Clyde, Dick Tracy and Bugsy, made his cinema debut in 1961's Splendor in the Grass?

6   Squaw Valley, the venue of the 1960 Winter Olympic Games, is in which US state? Colorado, Connecticut or California?

7   Which 1967 song includes the lyric "Sock it to me, sock it to me, sock it to me"?

8   In which 1969 film did Noel Coward play a prisoner called Mr Bridger?

9   Which actor, who played Rachel in the TV series Friends, was born in 1969 and, for five years, was married to Brad Pitt?

10 Which superpower enacted a long-running trade embargo against Cuba in February 1962?

Quiz 89

1   Who sang the theme tune to the 1964 Bond film, Goldfinger?

2   Which singer, who was sitting on the dock of the bay, is an anagram of "Driest Dingo"?

3   In which year did Alfred Hitchcock's The Birds hit cinemas? 1961, 1962 or 1963?

4   Which British TV cook was born in January 1960 and went on to write a book called How to Be a Domestic Goddess?

5   Who did John Lennon meet for the first time at London's Indica Gallery on 9 November 1966?

6   Who sang Strangers in the Night, which reached number 1 in 1966 in the UK, Italy, US, Germany, Ireland and Australia?

7   Who was the British Prime Minister at the start of the 1960s? Winston Churchill, Benjamin Disraeli or Harold Macmillan?

8   Which word appears most often in the Beatles' 1968 song Hey Jude? Jude, Nah or Hey?

9   What nationality was Che Guevara, a leader of the Cuban Revolution, who was assassinated in 1967? Cuban, Bolivian or Argentinian?

10 Which First Lady of the United States took television viewers on a tour of the White House in February 1962?

Quiz 90

1   Upon its launch in 1969, Concorde reduced the London to New York flight time from 8 hours to what? 3.5, 4.5 or 5.5 hours?

2   Rearrange the letters in "Customhouse Find" to spell out a popular musical of the 1960s.

3   Which TLH was a children's series about a dog that travelled from place to place solving peoples' problems?

4   In which 1967 film did Dustin Hoffman have the line "Mrs Robinson, you're trying to seduce me"?

5   Against which country did the town of Winnecone, Wisconsin, declare war in 1967? Cuba, the Soviet Union or the United States?

6   Which 1968-born Australian singer and actress has released albums including Body Language, X, Kiss Me Once and Aphrodite?

7   Which website was founded by 1966-born internet entrepreneur Jimmy Wales? eBay, Amazon or Wikipedia?

8   How much was the 1964 movie Goldfinger budgeted to cost? $3m, $30m or $300m?

9   Which country launched its first nuclear submarine, Redoubtable, in March 1967? Britain, France or Germany?

10   Name the 1966 film in which a submarine crew is shrunk to microscopic size and injected into the body of an injured scientist to repair his brain.

Quiz 91

1   Which US presidential candidate did Sirhan Sirhan assassinate in 1968?

2   Iran, Iraq, Kuwait, Saudi Arabia and Venezuela formed OPEC in September 1960. What does OPEC stand for?

3   By how many goals did England beat West Germany in the final of the 1966 FIFA World Cup?

4   Which British author's 1963 book was called The Spy Who Came in from The Cold?

5   Which city officially replaced Karachi as Pakistan's political capital in 1967?

6   Where is the Gateway Arch, which upon its completion in 1966 was the tallest man-made monument in the western hemisphere?

7   What was the name of the Beatles debut album, which was recorded at Abbey Road in February 1963?

8   By which performing name is 1961-born British singer George O'Dowd better known?

9   When was 2001: A Space Odyssey released to cinemas? 1964, 1966 or 1968?

10   What were the characters Pongo and Perdita, who were central to the plot of a 1961 Disney film?

Quiz 92

1 Which influential, slightly surreal TV series filmed in Portmeirion is an anagram of "Peter's Rhino"?

2 Who recorded the Motown record label's first number one, Please Mr Postman, which topped the charts in 1961?

3 Apollo 11 set off for the moon on 16 July 1969. How many days did it take it to arrive?

4 Which educational children's programme starring Big Bird and Elmo was first broadcast on 21 July 1969?

5 In which year were the films Lawrence of Arabia, The Manchurian Candidate and Dr No all released?

6 Along with Neil Armstrong and Buzz Aldrin, who was the third member of the Apollo 11 team that went to the moon?

7 Name the actor, born in 1965, who starred in Zoolander, Meet the Parents and There's Something About Mary.

8 Which year was MCMLXVIII when written in Roman numerals?

9 Which 1960 Chubby Checker song (with an associated dance craze) hit number 1 in the US charts and number 5 in the UK to become the year's third highest-grossing single?

10 What became available through the British National Health Service for the first time in December 1961? Organ transplants, cosmetic surgery or birth control pills?

Quiz 93

1 In 1969, who became the first man on the moon?

2 Which 1968-born Australian actor is known for his roles in Australia and Van Helsing, as well as playing Wolverine in the X-Men film series?

3 Who landed his first leading role in the 1964 spaghetti western, A Fistful of Dollars?

4   Which country accidentally dropped two hydrogen bombs on Spain, and one in the sea, when one of its bombers collided with a refuelling aircraft in January 1966? Britain, the United States or the Soviet Union?

5   Which former Nazi leader was abducted by Israeli agents in Buenos Aires in May 1960? Adolf Eichmann, Herman Goering or Albert Speer?

6   Who beat Hubert Humphrey to win the 1968 US presidential election?

7   On the subject of which world-shaking political event did the Warren Commission deliver the first official report in September 1964?

8   Which international broadcaster opened its brand new Television Centre in 1960, in the shape of a multi-story ring of studios and offices? NBC, CBS or the BBC?

9   Which lawyer, writer and former First Lady of the United States, was born in Chicago in 1964?

10   When did the Boeing 737 make its maiden flight? 1961, 1967 or 1969?

Quiz 94

1   In which year did Frank Sinatra release That's Life and Something Stupid? 1963, 1965 or 1967?

2   The Beatles' first film premiered in July 1964. Was it Help, Magical Mystery Tour, or A Hard Day's Night?

3   Name the 1960 film starring Frank Sinatra, Dean Martin and Sammy Davis Junior that was remade 41 years later starring George Clooney.

4   Which Italian city flooded to such an extent in 1966 that many ancient artworks and books were lost forever? Venice, Florence or Rome?

5   What was the name of Inspector Clouseau's man servant, played by Burt Kwouk, in the 1960s Pink Panther film series?

6   Which British singer did 1962-born Canadian filmmaker David Furnish marry in 2014?

7   Who became The Beatles' manager in January 1962 after Decca Records turned them down?

8   Penguin Books was found not guilty of obscenity in November 1960 for publishing which racy book by DH Lawrence?

9   Name the lead singer of the group Nirvana, who was born in 1967 and died, aged 27, in 1994.

10   The film Lawrence of Arabia, opens with a scene depicting Lawrence's funeral. How did he die? Motorcycle accident, Malaria or Malnutrition?

Quiz 95

1   Which actor, who would go on to star in the Indiana Jones and Star Wars films, made his cinema debut in 1966's Dead Heat on a Merry-Go-Round?

2   Dr Zhivago and The Sound of Music each received 10 Oscar nominations in 1965, and both went on to win an equal number, too. How many? Five, seven or nine?

3   What was the first film in which 1968-born English actor Daniel Craig played James Bond?

4   Who lived at 1313 Mockingbird Heights? The Flintstones, The Addams Family or The Munsters?

5   Which biography programme in which celebrities were surprised by a big red book and a parade of people from their past came to the end of its run in the US in 1961?

6   Which Scottish actor, who appeared on Broadway, in London's West End, and in films including Spy Kids and GoldenEye, was born in Perthshire in January 1965?

7   Who sang about The House of the Rising Sun in 1964?

8   Who played Eliza Doolittle in the 1964 film My Fair Lady?

Audrey Hepburn, Julie Andrews or Anne Bancroft?

9   Name the Irish-born singer-songwriter who had a smash hit in 1990 with Nothing Compares 2 U.

10   The first human in space died (on Earth) on 27 March 1968. Who was he?

Quiz 96

1   Which country hosted the 1964 Summer Olympics? China, Korea or Japan?

2   By what name is 1965-born musician Richard Melville Hall better known? His albums Go, 18 and Play were bestsellers on both sides of the Atlantic.

3   Which novelist of the Beat Generation wrote On the Road, a book about his travels across the United States, and died aged 47 in 1969?

4   Where was Lyndon B Johnson sworn in as president of the United States on 22 November 1963 following John F Kennedy's assassination?

5   Which gang were the rivals of the Jets in the 1961 film West Side Story?

6   Who was "Walkin' Back to Happiness" in 1961?

7   How many different people served as president of the United States at some point during the 1960s?

8   Who left the Supremes to go solo after the release of their 1969 single Someday We'll Be Together?

9   Who is James Bond sent to find and kill in the 1965 book The Man with the Golden Gun? Emile Largo, Auric Goldfinger or Francisco Scaramanga?

10   Which British actress won an Oscar for taking the lead in 1969 movie The Prime of Miss Jean Brodie?

Quiz 97

1 Who was James Earl Ray convicted of having assassinated on 4 April 1968?

2 Name the fictional spy created by 1963-born comedian Mike Myers who finds himself living in the present day, having been frozen during the mid-1960s.

3 Who was US president at the start of the 1960s?

4 What was the middle initial of Enterprise captain James Kirk of Star Trek?

5 The Farthing ceased to be legal tender in Britain on 31 December 1960. When had it first been issued? 13th century, 15th century or 17th century?

6 Which James Bond book did Ian Fleming publish in 1960? Octopussy, The Man with the Golden Gun or For Your Eyes Only?

7 Which Friends character was portrayed by 1964-born actor Courteney Cox?

8 At which 1969 New York state festival did The Who, Jefferson Airplane, Joan Baez, Joe Cocker, Santana, Janis Joplin and Jimi Hendrix all play?

9 Which CMC brought the world to the brink of nuclear war?

10 Which James Bond film, the third in the series, opened in UK cinemas in September 1964? Dr No, From Russia with Love or Goldfinger?

Quiz 98

1 Including six prototypes, how many Concorde aircraft were built in total? 20, 45 or 60?

2 What is the real first name of Buzz Aldrin, the second man on the moon?

3 Who was assassinated on 22 November 1963?

4   Which TSOM was a musical set in Second World War Austria?

5   Which puppet-based series, debuting in 1965, featured Jeff, Scott, John, Virgil, Gordon and Alan Tracy?

6   What was The Beatles' first single called? Love Me Do, Please Please Me or From Me To You?

7   Whose "I'm a Believer" was the second biggest-selling single of 1967?

8   When 1961-born Barack Obama became president of the United States, was he the 42nd, 44th or 46th person in that role?

9   Who played Mary Poppins in the 1964 film of the same name?

10   Which 1961-born Canadian starred in Back to the Future, Family Ties and Spin City and was diagnosed with early-onset Parkinson's disease in 1991?

Quiz 99

1   How old was John F Kennedy when he was assassinated in 1963? 44, 46 or 48?

2   How many of the four Oscars for which it was nominated at the 1964 Academy Awards did Stanley Kubrick's film Dr Strangelove win?

3   Rearrange the letters in "Canny Tsarina" to find the name of a popular singer with a famous father.

4   Who played the nuclear scientist, Dr Strangelove, in Stanley Kubrick's 1964 movie of the same name?

5   Which actor, from the films Interstellar, The Wedding Planner and Dallas Buyers Club, was born in Texas in November 1969?

6   For which 1964 film did Julie Andrews win the Academy Award for Best Actress?

7   Which sci-fi author co-wrote the 1968 film 2001: A Space

Odyssey with Stanley Kubrick?

8   Which Welsh future James Bond actor had his cinema debut in 1968 film The Lion in Winter?

9   Name the star ship originally captained by Christopher Pike in the pilot episode of Star Trek. Hint: it came under the command of James T Kirk from the very next episode.

10   Which James Bond book, featuring a plot in which SPECTRE steals two nuclear weapons, was published in 1961? Goldfinger, Thunderball or The World is Not Enough?

Quiz 100

1   Who did 1962-born Marcia Cross play in the series Desperate Housewives?

2   Which LA had a 1968 number one hit with What a Wonderful World?

3   Who assassinated John F Kennedy in Dallas in November 1963?

4   Which non-founding country was the first nation to apply to join the European Economic Community? Ireland, Sweden or the United Kingdom?

5   How many sports were competed in at the 1960 Winter Olympic Games? Four, 14 or 44?

6   Which boxer, born in Britain in 1965, defeated Mike Tyson in 2002 and fought Evander Holyfield twice in 1999?

7   Best known for writing Doctor Zhivago, which Soviet Russian novelist died in May 1960?

8   In 1969, who became the second man on the moon?

9   For which iconic film role was Roger Moore reportedly passed over in 1962 because he was "too young, perhaps a shade too pretty"?

10   What was Bagheera in the 1967 movie, The Jungle Book? A tiger, a panther or a bear?

Check out these other great quiz books from Ovingo
www.ovingo.com

Answers

Answers to quiz 1

1 Concorde
2 28
3 Mission: Impossible
4 Elvis Presley
5 Spider-Man
6 two and a half hours
7 China
8 Paul McCartney
9 Fred Flintstone
10 San Marino (Imola)

Answers to quiz 2

1 Six
2 Simon and Garfunkel
3 Mary Poppins
4 Procul Harum
5 TS Eliot
6 George Michael
7 Pool
8 747 (Jumbo Jet)
9 Omar Sharif
10 Porthmeirion

Answers to quiz 3

1 poet
2 four
3 Bob Dylan
4 The Pink Panther
5 Charles Dickens
6 Chile
7 False (Dwight D Eisenhower was)
8 Paul Anka
9 Harry Connick Jr
10 Daniel Craig

Answers to quiz 4

1 New Zealand
2 James Bond
3 Neil Armstrong
4 Barack Obama
5 Nicholas Cage
6 Three
7 The Rolling Stones
8 Bob Dylan
9 Tom and Jerry
10 Belfast

Answers to quiz 5

1 1960
2 Coronation Street
3 The Jetsons
4 Tiffany and Company (Tiffany's)
5 Frank Zappa
6 Germany
7 The Little Mermaid
8 Zulu
9 Robert F Kennedy
10 22,000 miles

Answers to quiz 6

1 Matthew Perry
2 U2
3 The Cavern Club
4 Jane and Michael
5 Tippi Hedren
6 a Volkswagen Beetle
7 Renee Zellweger
8 Spartacus
9 High Bonneville
10 Rudolf Nuryev

Answers to quiz 7

1 The Rolling Stones
2 42
3 1962
4 My Fair Lady
5 Concorde
6 Ice cream vans
7 Walt Disney
8 Neil Gaiman
9 The Supremes
10 Elizabeth Taylor

Answers to quiz 8

1 Jeremy Clarkson
2 Eddie Murphy
3 Winston Churchill
4 Bones
5 53
6 Oscar Hammerstein II
7 Twice
8 Peach
9 Nancy Sinatra
10 Brian Epstein

Answers to quiz 9

1 1969
2 Harper Lee
3 Mowgli
4 Danish
5 Stalingrad
6 Sam Mendes
7 Bridget Fonda
8 The Poseidon Adventure
9 Guy Pearce
10 New York

Answers to quiz 10

1 1962
2 Steptoe and Son
3 Japan
4 Bjork
5 Patsy Cline
6 Memphis
7 Anthony Burgess
8 Pussy Galore
9 The Addams Family
10 Go into space

Answers to quiz 11

1 Bullitt
2 Rudolf Nuryev
3 smoking
4 Kim Philby
5 The Mousetrap
6 Boston
7 Ally McBeal
8 Tom Jones
9 The Edge
10 Hawaii Five-O

Answers to quiz 12

1 Martin Luther King Jr
2 Segregation
3 Geneva
4 The Magic Roundabout (The Magic Carousel in the US)
5 Apple
6 Andy Warhol
7 Jane Horrocks
8 Bono
9 Stalin
10 John Wyndham

Answers to quiz 13

1 David Cameron
2 Sarah Jessica Parker
3 Cassius Clay
4 Porsche
5 Bengal tiger
6 Cuba Gooding Jr
7 South Africa
8 Gene Hackman
9 France
10 1967

Answers to quiz 14

1 Eva Cassidy
2 Dana Scully
3 1961
4 Rob Lowe
5 Dr Strangelove
6 Leonard Bernstein and Stephen Sondheim
7 Ian McKellen
8 Colin Firth
9 Sarah Palin
10 Peter O'Toole

Answers to quiz 15

1 Lincoln
2 Rome
3 John Lennon
4 Michael Caine
5 Czechoslovakia
6 Blade Runner
7 Jane Leeves
8 Simon & Garfunkel
9 Che Guevara
10 What's New Pussycat?

Answers to quiz 16

1 Enid Blyton
2 Whitney Houston
3 50s
4 The Rolling Stones
5 Buzz Aldrin
6 Heather Locklear
7 Kylie Minogue
8 Baz Luhrmann
9 I Want to Hold Your Hand
10 Teacher

Answers to quiz 17

1 Mia Farrow
2 The Internet
3 The Village
4 Swedish
5 von Trapp
6 Christopher Walken
7 AstroTurf
8 France
9 Return to Sender
10 Jonny Cash

Answers to quiz 18

1 Alistair MacLean
2 Julia Sawalha
3 Elvis Presley
4 Amazon
5 Officer Dibble
6 two years
7 Bret Easton Ellis
8 1963
9 Zebra
10 Personal computer

Answers to quiz 19

1. Chitty-Chitty-Bang-Bang
2. Pamela Anderson
3. 13
4. The Sound of Music
5. Patsy Cline
6. David Duchovny
7. Beginners' All-purpose Symbolic Instruction Code
8. Chairman
9. Antonio Banderas
10. Ho Chi Minh

Answers to quiz 20

1. Lady Chatterley's Lover
2. Stanley Kubrick
3. The Fugitive
4. United Kingdom
5. 3
6. Algeria
7. The Thomas Crown Affair
8. Norman Bates
9. Please Mr Postman
10. Three (1960, 1964, 1968)

Answers to quiz 21

1. Stalin
2. John Lennon
3. Dustin Hoffman
4. Von Ryan's Express
5. Otis Redding
6. Sarah Brightman
7. Yuri Gagarin
8. I Dream of Jeannie
9. The Addams Family
10. From Russia with Love

Answers to quiz 22

1. Steve Coogan
2. Work an extra half hour every day for no pay
3. Three (but it actually ran for four)
4. Pebbles
5. A Little Prayer
6. Elizabeth Taylor
7. Sean Penn
8. Heart
9. Ben-Hur
10. Ford

Answers to quiz 23

1. Britt Ekland
2. Cleopatra
3. ...the Sundance Kid
4. The Animals
5. San Francisco
6. My Fair Lady
7. The French Lieutenant's Woman
8. Vienna
9. Miss Marple
10. Oh, Pretty Woman

Answers to quiz 24

1. Cocaine
2. John Lennon
3. JJ Abrams
4. Republic of Ireland
5. Nancy Sinatra
6. The Byrds
7. Garry Kasparov
8. Ian Fleming
9. Michael Douglas
10. Zip codes (postal codes)

Answers to quiz 25

1　Celine Dion
2　Matthew Broderick
3　Pussy Galore
4　United Kingdom
5　It's Now or Never, and Are You Lonesome Tonight
6　Cleopatra
7　Fred Quimby
8　Jim Morrison
9　Vanilla Ice
10　Mini

Answers to quiz 26

1　London Bridge
2　The Berlin Wall
3　Iraq
4　Felicity Huffman
5　The Littlest Hobo
6　Catch-22
7　Berliner
8　Matthew Broderick
9　John F Kennedy
10　New York

Answers to quiz 27

1　her head (it was a hairstyle)
2　Ally McBeal
3　The Supremes
4　Two
5　Apollo
6　Quentin Tarantino
7　Lenny Kravitz
8　Helena Bonham Carter
9　Austria
10　Because if you rotate it 180 degrees it still says 1961

Answers to quiz 28

1　Paula Abdul
2　1960
3　Nixon (19 years)
4　Toni Braxton
5　Muhammad Ali
6　Canada
7　Ian Rankin
8　Lieutenant (Nyota) Uhura
9　Eric Carle
10　Marilyn Monroe

Answers to quiz 29

1　He had been shot
2　Professor Christiaan Barnard
3　Fight Club
4　Kuwait
5　The Beatles
6　The Benny Hill Show
7　Shania Twain
8　Enya
9　before
10　Judi Dench

Answers to quiz 30

1　3
2　Michael Stipe
3　Breakfast at Tiffany's
4　the mouse
5　MC Escher
6　It's the location on the moon where Armstrong stepped out of the Apollo 11 capsule
7　1962
8　Catherine Oxenberg
9　Czechoslovakia
10　She was the first person to die while trying to cross the Berlin Wall

Answers to quiz 31

1 Otis Redding
2 1964
3 It switched from driving on the left to driving on the right
4 21
5 12.30pm
6 Rawhide
7 three (Lincoln, Garfield, McKinley)
8 Cliff Richard
9 before
10 Edinburgh

Answers to quiz 32

1 United Kingdom
2 Cliff Richard
3 Brad Pitt
4 Sgt Pepper's Lonely Hearts Club Band
5 Goldie Hawn
6 Leonid Brezhnev
7 Axl Rose
8 Harpo
9 Wednesday
10 Arnold Schwarzenegger

Answers to quiz 33

1 1964
2 Herbie
3 Donald Campbell
4 Nikita Khrushchev
5 Matt LeBlanc
6 the miniskirt
7 Alfred Hitchcock
8 Gabriel Garciz Marquez
9 Lee Harvey Oswald
10 United States

Answers to quiz 34

1 Kennedy (2 years, 306 days)
2 Mary Poppins
3 France
4 Anthony Burgess
5 Chris Evans
6 Dick Van Dyke
7 Muriel Spark
8 Greece
9 29
10 Mike Tyson

Answers to quiz 35

1 The Spy Who Came in from the Cold
2 Roz Doyle
3 Tom Cruise
4 Yellow Submarine
5 George Formby
6 Charlie Chaplin
7 Cindy Crawford
8 Outer Space Treaty
9 Taco Bell
10 Soviet Citizen (Russian)

Answers to quiz 36

1 Perry Mason
2 Kirk Douglas
3 Richard Burton
4 Carry on Constable
5 Sonny and Cher
6 a horse
7 West Side Story
8 Muammar Gaddafi
9 Virginia Wade
10 a gulag

Answers to quiz 37

1 Simon and Garfunkel
2 It was the first Olympic mascott, at the Games in Grenoble
3 Linda Eastman
4 The Beatles
5 The Rolling Stones
6 101
7 Jennifer Lopez
8 A satellite
9 Lawrence of Arabia
10 Dusty Springfield

Answers to quiz 38

1 The Righteous Brothers
2 Helen Keller
3 Doctor Zhivago
4 Vietnam
5 Michael Caine
6 Stanley Kubrick
7 Mary Quant
8 Sparrow
9 Charlie Sheen
10 Farrah Fawcett

Answers to quiz 39

1 Marilyn Monroe
2 The Sound of Music
3 Julia Roberts
4 Jodie Foster
5 Lisa Marie Presley
6 The Beatles
7 Rupert Murdoch
8 Star Trek
9 Nicole Kidman
10 Fidel Castro (Cuba)

Answers to quiz 40

1 Woody Harrelson
2 Timothy Dalton
3 Boris Karloff
4 Christian Slater
5 Midnight Cowboy
6 Dad's Army
7 French
8 David Jones
9 Vanessa Williams
10 An aircraft

Answers to quiz 41

1 Lufthansa
2 Rufus Sewell
3 Susan Boyle
4 50
5 John Steinbeck
6 1960
7 The Supremes
8 Jim Clark
9 Mick Hucknall
10 Paleontologist

Answers to quiz 42

1 Lisa Kudrow
2 Nat King Cole
3 Ursula Andress
4 Mona Lisa
5 Lee Harvey Oswald
6 Northern Ireland
7 150mph
8 Guns N Roses
9 Will Smith
10 The Pink Panther

Answers to quiz 43

1 England
2 Le Corbusier
3 30
4 Big Mac
5 West Side Story
6 Ken
7 Billy Zane
8 Truman Capote
9 Yasser Arafat
10 Teri Hatcher

Answers to quiz 44

1 Ford
2 Czechoslovakia
3 United Kingdom
4 John Cleese
5 Desi Arnaz
6 Richard Rodgers and Oscar Hammerstein
7 Gary Cooper
8 Slash
9 The Ronettes
10 Chitty Chitty Bang Bang: The Magical Car

Answers to quiz 45

1 West Side Story
2 Vivien Leigh
3 France
4 Kim Wilde
5 39
6 Niagra Falls
7 Procul Harum
8 Helen Mirren
9 The Righteous Brothers
10 Sheryl Crow

Answers to quiz 46

1 Petula Clark
2 1962
3 Peter Sellers
4 Maya Angelou
5 Charlie and the Chocolate Factory
6 2001: A Space Odyssey
7 Nelson Mandela
8 Martin Luther King Jr
9 Rick Astley
10 Britain

Answers to quiz 47

1 Brazilian
2 women
3 8
4 Ford
5 James Bond's Aston Martin DB5
6 Jean-Claude Van Damme
7 Nevil Shute
8 Louis Armstrong
9 Sgt Pepper's Lonely Hearts Club Band
10 Vietnam

Answers to quiz 48

1 Switzerland
2 Winston Churchill
3 The Italian Job
4 Greece
5 Holly
6 The Dirty Dozen
7 Butch Cassidy and the Sundance Kid
8 CS Lewis
9 The Rolling Stones
10 35th

Answers to quiz 49

1 Telstar
2 One Hundred and One Dalmatians
3 Burt Reynolds
4 Israel
5 Flipper
6 35
7 Morgan Freeman
8 France
9 Cleopatra
10 The Grand Tour

Answers to quiz 50

1 Marine Le Pen
2 Oliver Twist
3 Sonny and Cher
4 Canadian
5 Bob Dylan
6 Danish
7 The World Trade Center
8 Sandra Bullock
9 Bonnie and Clyde
10 Czechoslovakia

Answers to quiz 51

1 Toby Stephens
2 Gary Coleman
3 James Nesbitt
4 Boeing 747
5 Top Gun
6 Clement Attlee
7 Bridget Fonda
8 Big Mac
9 The Cavern Club
10 Marcia Cross

Answers to quiz 52

1 Sgt Pepper's Lonely Hearts Club Band
2 1966
3 Turin
4 Three billion
5 Gap
6 Cuba
7 Edith Piaf
8 Al Pacino
9 The Beach Boys
10 The Coca-Cola Company

Answers to quiz 53

1 Yoko Ono
2 Democratic
3 Lava Lamp
4 Monty Python's Flying Circus
5 Egypt
6 Friday
7 The Man from U.N.C.L.E.
8 The laser printer
9 United Nations Secretary-General
10 Robert Carlyle

Answers to quiz 54

1 The Beatles
2 Cilla Black
3 Daphne Moon
4 Mary Poppins
5 Peter Jackson
6 the United States and Soviet Union
7 Joseph and the Amazing Technicolor Dreamcoat
8 September
9 pigs
10 1964

Answers to quiz 55

1 Raymond Burr
2 Roman
3 Harper Lee
4 Frank Sinatra
5 Oliver
6 Kimble
7 Johnny Depp
8 Hal
9 36
10 Christopher Eccleston

Answers to quiz 56

1 Paint Your Wagon
2 Jonathan Ive
3 Help
4 Joanne Harris
5 Bedrock
6 kd lang
7 Bob Dylan
8 Paris
9 Steffi Graf
10 False: it was 1959

Answers to quiz 57

1 Israel
2 Lady Chatterley's Lover
3 New Zealand
4 Lady Penelope
5 Herbert Hoover
6 Jungle Book
7 Dallas
8 The Flintstones
9 Eleanor Roosevelt
10 Barbra Streisand

Answers to quiz 58

1 Keanu Reeves
2 Teri Hatcher
3 The Doors
4 Brian Epstein
5 Michael Hutchence
6 Tracy Chapman
7 630ft (190m)
8 Michael Schumacher
9 Birth control
10 My Fair Lady

Answers to quiz 59

1 Ernest Hemingway
2 Mary Poppins
3 Brooke Shields
4 Stanley Kibrick
5 France and Germany
6 Robert Downey Jr
7 A hotel
8 1961
9 Eisenhower (62)
10 Tokyo

Answers to quiz 60

1 United States
2 Malcolm X
3 Keifer Sutherland
4 Judy Garland
5 The cover of the Beatles album Sgt Pepper's Lonely Hearts Club Band
6 France
7 Yugoslavia
8 The Beatles
9 Puppet on a String
10 Intel

Answers to quiz 61

1   Jimmy Osmond
2   Hawaii Five-O
3   Criminal defense lawyer
4   Sean Connery
5   Hugh Grant
6   The Channel Tunnel
7   Simon and Garfunkel
8   Evil Knievel
9   India
10 John Steinbeck

Answers to quiz 62

1   Los Angeles
2   United Kingdom
3   Stockholm
4   The Graduate
5   Are You Lonesome Tonight
6   Patrick Troughton
7   New Orleans
8   Cilla Black
9   He was elected pope (Pope Paul VI)
10 Jennifer Rush

Answers to quiz 63

1   IMAX
2   Sean Connery
3   Hawaii
4   Stanley Kubrick
5   Damian Hurst
6   60%
7   Pussy Galore
8   Ronald Reagan
9   Steve Irwin
10 Damon Albarn

Answers to quiz 64

1   Janet Jackson
2   Cate Blanchett
3   Patrick McGoohan
4   10
5   Dune
6   The Who
7   Bay of Pigs
8   Spacecraft (Apollo 7)
9   Michael Dell
10 The Godfather

Answers to quiz 65

1   Julia Gillard
2   Top Cat
3   32
4   The Pink Panther
5   True
6   The Munsters
7   Alan Shephard
8   It's Now or Never
9   Richard Nixon
10 Daryll Hannah

Answers to quiz 66

1   J Robert Oppenheimer
2   Cole Porter
3   Richard Nixon
4   United States
5   Month Python's Flying Circus
6   A computer operating system
7   Revolver
8   Tom Hollander
9   Mexico
10 Rio de Janeiro

Answers to quiz 67

1 Number Six
2 Doctor Zhivago
3 39
4 Demi Moore
5 British (Princess Margaret)
6 Easy Rider
7 Donald Sutherland
8 Ricky Gervais
9 Raquel Welch
10 Chairman Mao Zedong

Answers to quiz 68

1 The Beach Boys
2 Butch Cassidy and the Sundance Kid
3 Day Tripper
4 Chitty Chitty Bang Bang: The Magical Car
5 Stuart Sutcliffe
6 1964
7 Buster Keaton
8 Eric Cantona
9 Procul Harum
10 San Francisco

Answers to quiz 69

1 United Kingdom
2 Samuel Beckett
3 Priest
4 Kristin Scott Thomas
5 Bridget Jones
6 The Graduate
7 Romania
8 Gone with the Wind
9 Mary Quant
10 George Clooney

Answers to quiz 70

1 Votes for women / universal suffrage
2 Paul Newman
3 19
4 Berlin
5 Julie Andrews
6 Portugal
7 Diana, Princess of Wales
8 Chairman Mao Zedong
9 Ireland
10 Tommy

Answers to quiz 71

1 Gregory Peck
2 True (in seasons 4 and 5)
3 Julie Andrews
4 David Lynch
5 The Man from U.N.C.L.E.
6 Dr No
7 Detroit
8 Andrew
9 The Sound of Music
10 James May

Answers to quiz 72

1 Carla Bruni
2 Martin Luther King Jr
3 Oklahoma City
4 West Germany
5 A dolphin
6 A pink diamond
7 Juliette Binoche
8 Curtis Stigers
9 JK Rowling
10 CS Forester

Answers to quiz 73

1 Munich
2 Michael Hutchence
3 Jack Ruby
4 1964
5 Leonard Nimoy
6 George Lazenby
7 Fidel Castro
8 11
9 Fox Mulder
10 Samantha

Answers to quiz 74

1 Blackbird
2 A VW Beetle car
3 FBI Special Agent
4 John F Kennedy
5 Jim Carrey
6 The Incredible Hulk
7 The Final Frontier
8 Telstar
9 Diana Rigg
10 True (and $1,000 and $5,000 bills)

Answers to quiz 75

1 Lambourghini
2 10cm
3 Cliff Richard
4 It was the building from which Lee Harvey Oswald shot President Kennedy
5 Philips
6 United Kingdom
7 It went from having 49 to 50 stars
8 Christopher Plummer
9 Eastman
10 Four

Answers to quiz 76

1 The Jungle Book
2 Germany and Japan
3 12
4 Catch-18
5 Evelyn Waugh
6 Split screen
7 Bono
8 Lyndon B Johnson
9 Guy Ritchie
10 Lockheed U-2 spy plane

Answers to quiz 77

1 Rosemary's Baby
2 1960s (three leap years; the others had two)
3 Prince Andrew
4 Spartacus
5 Lybia
6 Laurie Lee
7 Marilyn Monroe
8 Iran
9 Winston Churchill
10 Clark Gable

Answers to quiz 78

1 Perry Mason
2 1968
3 WWF (World Wide Fund for Nature)
4 Nikita Khrushchev
5 Vice President of the United States
6 1960
7 Concorde
8 Nevil Shute
9 Muslim
10 Noel Gallagher

Answers to quiz 79

1 John Lennon
2 Daniel O'Donnell
3 Alfred Hitchcock
4 US president John F Kennedy
5 The Animals
6 Psycho
7 Yellow Submarine
8 Mika Hakkinen
9 Commissioner Dreyfus
10 Salzburg

Answers to quiz 80

1 The Prisoner
2 Motown
3 Spanish
4 Funny Girl
5 5
6 Putting a man on the moon
7 Mayalsia
8 Abbey Road
9 The Byrds
10 Anthony Hopkins

Answers to quiz 81

1 Gordon Ramsay
2 Spencer
3 The Saint
4 Gone With The Wind
5 Alan Alda
6 Ralph Feinnes
7 Las Vegas
8 34
9 Hair
10 John McCain

Answers to quiz 82

1 Hawaii
2 Ich Bin Ein Berliner
3 One Flew Over the Cuckoo's Nest
4 Abbey Road
5 London
6 Fidel Castro
7 Domino's Pizza
8 Mashed Potato
9 24
10 Breakfast at Tiffany's

Answers to quiz 83

1 The Odd Couple
2 Seal
3 The Addams Family
4 Nanny
5 Plane crash
6 The FIFA World Cup Trophy (called the Jules Rimet Trophy at the time)
7 Dealey
8 Sarah Jessica Parker
9 Please Mr Postman
10 Hair

Answers to quiz 84

1 Len Deighton
2 The Rolling Stones
3 Mexico 1968
4 Joseph Heller
5 Wallander
6 Once
7 United Kingdom
8 Soviet Union
9 Anne Bancroft
10 Jeopardy

Answers to quiz 85

1 Sunday
2 I Heard it Through the Grapevine
3 Pink Floyd
4 Joe Orton
5 Austria
6 Wet Wet Wet
7 The Beatles
8 Star Trek
9 Robert F Kennedy
10 Lucille Ball

Answers to quiz 86

1 United Kingdom
2 False (he was elected in 1974)
3 Northern Rhodesia
4 John Lennon
5 FBI
6 Flowers
7 A cat
8 whirlpool hot tub baths
9 Jenny Agutter
10 The Tornados

Answers to quiz 87

1 South Africa
2 Jacqueline Kennedy
3 Catherine Zeta-Jones
4 The Avengers
5 Pink Floyd
6 The Pentagon
7 The landing of the Apollo 11 capsule on the moon
8 1967
9 Daphne du Maurier
10 UK

Answers to quiz 88

1 John F Kennedy
2 The Space Needle
3 Elizabeth Hurley
4 Wes Anderson
5 Warren Beaty
6 California
7 Respect by Aretha Franklin
8 The Italian Job
9 Jennifer Aniston
10 United States

Answers to quiz 89

1 Shirley Bassey
2 Otis Redding
3 1963
4 Nigella Lawson
5 Yoko Ono
6 Frank Sinatra
7 Harold Macmillan
8 Nah
9 Argentinian
10 Jacqueline Kennedy

Answers to quiz 90

1 3.5 hours
2 The Sound of Music
3 The Littlest Hobo
4 The Graduate
5 United States
6 Kylie Minogue
7 Wikipedia
8 $3m
9 France
10 Fantastic Voyage

Answers to quiz 91

1 Robert Kennedy
2 Organisation of the Petroleum Exporting Countries
3 Two (the score was 4-2 to England)
4 John Le Carre
5 Islamabad
6 St Louis
7 Please Please Me
8 Boy George
9 1968
10 Dalmatians

Answers to quiz 92

1 The Prisoner
2 The Marvelettes
3 4 (20th July)
4 Sesame Street
5 1962
6 Michael Collins
7 Ben Stiller
8 1968
9 The Twist
10 Birth control pills

Answers to quiz 93

1 Neil Armstrong
2 Hugh Jackman
3 Clint Eastwood
4 United States
5 Adolf Eichman
6 Richard Nixon
7 The assassination of president John F Kennedy
8 The BBC
9 Michelle Obama
10 1967

Answers to quiz 94

1 1967
2 A Hard Day's Night
3 Ocean's 11
4 Florence
5 Cato
6 Elton John
7 Brian Epstein
8 Lady Chatterley's Lover
9 Kurt Cobain
10 Motorcycle accident

Answers to quiz 95

1 Harrison Ford
2 Five
3 Casino Royale
4 The Munsters
5 This is Your Life
6 Alan Cumming
7 The Animals
8 Audrey Hepburn
9 Sinead O'Connor
10 Yuri Gagarin

Answers to quiz 96

1 Japan
2 Moby
3 Jack Kerouac
4 Air Force One
5 The Sharks
6 Helen Shapiro
7 4 (Eisenhower, Kennedy, Johnson, Nixon)
8 Diana Ross
9 Francisco Scaramanga
10 Maggie Smith

Answers to quiz 97

1 Martin Luther King Jr
2 Austin Powers
3 Dwight D Eisenhower
4 T
5 13th century
6 For Your Eyes Only
7 Monica Geller
8 Woodstock
9 Cuban Missile Crisis
10 Goldfinger

Answers to quiz 98

1 20
2 Edwin
3 John F Kennedy
4 The Sound of Music
5 Thunderbirds
6 Love Me Do
7 The Monkees
8 44th
9 Julie Andrews
10 Michael J Fox

Answers to quiz 99

1 46
2 None
3 Nancy Sinatra
4 Peter Sellers
5 Matthew McConaughey
6 Mary Poppins
7 Arthur C Clarke
8 Timothy Dalton
9 Enterprise
10 Thunderball

Answers to quiz 100

1 Bree Van Der Kamp
2 Louis Armstrong
3 Lee Harvey Oswald
4 Ireland
5 Four
6 Lennox Lewis
7 Boris Pasternak
8 Buzz Aldrin
9 James Bond
10 A panther

Check out these other great quiz books from Ovingo
www.ovingo.com

Made in the USA
Middletown, DE
22 November 2022

15759013R00059